A SUDDEN ENGAGEMENT

As a budding actress, Kirsty had no reason to love the drama critic Drew Chalmers, who with one blistering review had almost wrecked her promising career. So how was it that she now found herself having to pretend to be engaged to him?

A SUDDEN ENGAGEMENT

BY
PENNY JORDAN

MILLS & BOON LIMITED
15–16 BROOK'S MEWS
LONDON W1A 1DR

First published 1983
Australian copyright 1983
Philippine copyright 1983
This edition 1983

© Penny Jordan 1983

ISBN 0 263 74268 7

Set in Monophoto Plantin 11 on 11½ pt.
01-0683 - 47474

Made and printed in Great Britain by
Richard Clay (The Chaucer Press) Ltd,
Bungay, Suffolk

CHAPTER ONE

THEIR play was going to close. Somehow Kirsty knew it; she could taste the bitter flavour of defeat, had sensed from the audience response that all was not going well. Her meagre savings were almost exhausted and unless she found an office job to tide her over she would have to go tail between her legs back to her parents.

If only Chelsea and Slade weren't away in Italy! Much as she loved her parents, her mother was inclined to fuss, and indeed had never wanted her to become an actress. Her aunt, though, understood. An actress; Kirsty grimaced wryly, slipping out of the theatre without bothering to join the others in the green room. If it hadn't been for Drew Chalmers' biting criticism of her in her last play she might still have been appearing in it; might indeed have gone with it to New York with the rest of the cast.

As the icy cold wind, unseasonal in September, funnelled down the collar of her suede coat she shivered and tried to huddle deeper into it. The coat had been a present from her aunt and her new husband the previous Christmas, and a very welcome one. The soft cream suede suited her dark curls and faintly olive-tinged skin and the expensive cut flattered her curvy shape; slightly less curvy of late. The salary she was being paid by the small theatre group she was now working for barely covered her rent and the basics; and just for a moment she allowed herself to think weakeningly of her mother's delicious cooking; of the meal that had always been waiting for her when she lived at home.

She was the one who had wanted to leave, she reminded herself. If her mother had had her way she would still be living in Melchester, still going out with the boy next door, marriage ultimately on the cards when he finished university, but much as she liked him she hadn't wanted that.

For as long as she could remember she had wanted to act, had dreamed of acting, but always the very great parts, she acknowledged ruefully, and she had firmly believed that she could succeed in her chosen career. Her drama school teachers had encouraged her, and she had been over the moon when she had got her very first role; a small part, admittedly, but in a very prestigious work by an up-and-coming play-wright. Now she could acknowledge that she had never felt truly at home in the role—that of a street-wise teenager, cynical and worldly. It had called for a depth of experience she now realised she lacked, and although she had done her best, and had been reasonably satisfied with the result, the sardonic and powerful critic who had reviewed the first night had been scathing in his denunciation of her interpretation of the role. 'Small-town and small-time', had been the most least offensive of his comments, and after reading his harsh denunciation of her Kirsty hadn't been surprised to learn that she was no longer needed on the cast.

Since then she had spent six long months looking for work before she had got her present part; a very small walk-on one in fringe theatre, and strangely enough she now felt that she had gained the experience needed to play her lost part far better.

Quite why Drew Chalmers had made her the object of his acid attack she didn't know; she would have thought herself far too lowly to merit such attention. One of the cast had suggested it might have something to do with the fact that he and the playwright Nigel Evans were acknowledged rivals. God, how she had hated him! Still hated him, she acknowledged honestly. But for Drew Chalmers she would now be appearing on Broadway, gaining the experience she needed if other theatrical doors were not to be barred to her. Chelsea had sympathised, but sympathy only went so far, and Kirsty knew anyway that her aunt did not have her passionate love for the stage, for all that she had originally trained for it. What hurt the most was that she knew that he had been right; she had not been up to the part, and his condemnation of her as a 'small-town girl incapable of convincing any audience that she was anything other than exactly that, and second rate small town into the bargain' still rankled.

It was almost a mile from the small dilapidated theatre the group had hired to Kirsty's lodgings, and as she waited to cross the main road she noticed the long, sleekly expensive car hurtling past her. Its occupants would be going to dine and dance at the exclusive hotel on the edge of the town, made famous by its superlative golf course, no doubt. A small smile twisted her pretty mouth, as a sudden impulse took root in her mind. Why not? She needed something to cheer herself up, and there was still that birthday cheque she had received from Chelsea and Slade which she had been carefully hoarding for a rainy day. Why not go mad and splurge the lot? Caution and impulse warred and suddenly impulse won. She deserved a treat, Kirsty told herself firmly. She would go back to her lodgings, change, then take a taxi to the hotel and treat herself to a first-class meal and a night in the most luxurious accommodation the town could provide!

By the time she had reached her lodgings, a terraced house set in a miserable terrace of similar houses, bleak and unwelcoming on this unpleasant September evening, caution had prevailed to the extent that she had promised herself that if a phone call to the hotel elicited the response that no rooms were available she would forget the whole idea. However, she was in luck, or out of it, dependent upon one's view, and the receptionist assured her cheerfully that yes, indeed, they had a room and that of course it was possible to book it for a single night.

Mrs Larch, her landlady, looked pained and curious when Kirsty told her she was going out to dinner and wouldn't be returning that night.

'Boy-friend, is it?' she enquired, eyeing Kirsty assessingly. 'Like I told you when I gave you a room, I don't hold with those sort of carryings on. Always been a decent house, this has, and always will be. . . .'

In spite of her landlady's avid curiosity, Kirsty managed to escape to her room without giving anything away.

Her mother would throw a fit if she could see her room, she reflected ruefully as she opened the door. The wallpaper was shabby and faded, the room heated by a miserly two-bar electric fire. The bed was narrow and lumpy; an old-fashioned wardrobe far too large and dark for the small room. No cooking was allowed in the rooms, but despite that Kirsty had managed to smuggle in a toaster, which together with her electric kettle meant that at least she could always have a cup of coffee and a piece of toast. But she was going to do better than toast and coffee tonight—much better! Now, what was she going to wear?

She opened the wardrobe and surveyed its contents thoughtfully. Thanks to her aunt she had several attractive outfits. One of them in particular caught her eye—a soft cream silk dress. Her mother had protested that at barely twenty she was far too young to wear anything so sophisticated when she had seen it, but she had fallen in love with it, and had refused to be placated with anything else.

She was lucky enough to find the bathroom unoccupied and the water almost warm—tonight she would lie for hours and hours in her very own bathroom, she promised herself, simply soaking in lovely hot, perfumed water. The silk slid softly over her newly washed and perfumed skin, the front dipping almost to the waist, revealing the swelling curves of her breasts, the cleverly draped neckline making the plunge alluring rather than obvious. The deep vee was repeated at the back before the dress teased and tantalised with full-length, close-fitting sleeves and a skirt that moved against her skin in silken ripples, caressing her body from hip to knee.

It was a dress that to another woman was instantly recognisable as very sexy, but to a man, conditioned to equate 'sexy' with 'little black numbers', it was quite plain, until it was seen on, preferably on a woman who knew how to walk properly, as Kirsty now did.

Her dark hair curled naturally and normally she left it down on her shoulders, but tonight she swept it upwards into a softly flattering style, adding the pearl and diamond earrings and the matching necklace that had been a bridesmaid present to her on the occasion of Chelsea and Slade's wedding.

Kirsty smiled impishly as she thought of her aunt—nearer her own age than her mother's and a close and valued friend. She wished they weren't quite so far away, but her small godson's arrival had left his mother a little tired and her doting husband had swept mother and baby off to Italy for peace and quiet before 'the whole family descend on us for Christmas', as he had put it succinctly to Kirsty before they left.

Kirsty liked Slade. Her aunt needed a man strong enough to curb her wilful streak and compassionate enough to understand her more vulnerable side, and in Slade she had found one. She and Chelsea were very alike, Kirsty admitted.

She too had that same impulsive wilfulness that could flare up out of nowhere, and sometimes change the whole pattern of planned events. Like the time Chelsea and Slade had first met, and Chelsea had mistakenly thought that Kirsty was in love with him, and had decided to rescue her. A grin curved her mouth, bringing warmth to the sparkling brown depths of her eyes. Her skin, naturally matt and smooth, needed no foundation, but her training had taught her the importance of good make-up, so she applied blusher, and added mascara and the merest hint of coffee eyeshadow to add a mysterious allure to the slightly Oriental slant of her eyes, darkening her lips with a pretty gloss before slipping on slim-heeled leather shoes and picking up her red coat.

The taxi arrived on time, and Kirsty had to repress another grin as she saw the betraying movement of the lace curtains at the front window as she was driven away.

No doubt the rest of the cast would be in the pub now discussing the débâcle of the latest performance; even if they decided to go on she knew she could not. Playing a punk teenager, disenchanted with life, delivering lines in heavily interspersed with four-letter words and possessing very little other merit, had lost its appeal. Putting to use the secretarial skills her parents had insisted she learn would almost be a relief, and there would be other parts, she promised herself as the town centre was left behind and they began to drive from the more exclusive suburbs.

Winton was a small seaside town, close enough

to Bournemouth to consider itself 'select' but yet somehow lacking the flair and panache which would have made it so. It was a town of retired schoolteachers and ex-soldiers, and surely the worst possible place on earth to launch a play dealing with the raw reality of life in Toxteth and the effect of environment on upbringing, which was the theme of the play, and one which Kirsty thought was very worthwhile, but somehow Bernard Wray's interpretation of it lacked impact. Kirsty wasn't too happy with his reliance on violence both in language and in actions to get across his message, but then she hadn't written the play and he had, and the others seemed quite happy. She was too romantic, Kirsty acknowledged as the taxi took the coast road. All through her schooldays she had dreamed of the great Shakespearean roles, the Restoration comedies, the wit and laughter that lingered in these and the Noël Coward plays like the sharp, clean scent of lavender. Who amongst the modern playwrights could rival those giants?

Lost in her thoughts, Kirsty suddenly realised that her taxi was turning into the approach to the hotel.

Built in the full flush of Edwardian splendour, it had a shrub-lined drive, and the early September dusk hid from her the lawned gardens and golf course which the hotel boasted. A uniformed commissionnaire opened the taxi door for her, and suddenly throwing herself into her new role, Kirsty tipped the driver recklessly, bestowing on him a smile that transformed her gamin features and made him stare at her in stunned appreciation.

The hotel foyer was thickly carpeted; several business-suited men wandered about, mingling with the older guests who were obviously hotel residents. Kirsty gave her name to the smiling receptionist, who indicated the way to the dining room and its intimate bar, where several couples were already enjoying pre-dinner drinks. The Edwardian ambience of the hotel was underlined by the bar and dining room, referred to by the receptionist as the 'Palm Court Suite'.

Clever lighting emphasised the skilled and effective *trompe l'œuil* work on the walls and ceiling—if she hadn't known better Kirsty could almost have been persuaded that beyond the delicate trelliswork on the walls actually lay that perfect blue sea and matching sky, so persuasive was the illusion of a Mediterranean shore depicted on the walls. The theme was carried through with attractive white 'terrace-style' furniture, and as she ordered a pre-dinner cocktail from the mouthwateringly tempting selection Kirsty started to study her fellow diners.

Studying human nature was a fascinating pursuit, and as always the actress in her was searching eagerly for mannerisms and expressions to add to her repertoire.

When her cocktail arrived it tasted delicious, worth every penny of the exorbitant price she had seen listed beside it; a pale banana-yellow frothy delight that reminded her of a grown-up version of her favourite milk shakes. It was also extremely potent, and by the time the head waiter appeared discreetly at her side to tell her that her table was ready Kirsty was beginning to feel distinctly lightheaded.

She had been skipping lunches recently; a reminder not to drink when she was doing so, she told herself as she studied her menu avidly.

Selfconsciousness had never been one of her faults; no one aspiring to be a successful actress could be, and consequently she felt no embarrassment at dining alone, oblivious to the appreciative looks she was getting from the male occupants of other tables as she pored over her menu, totally absorbed in the difficult task of making the right choice.

At last she decided on a seafood platter followed by tournedos Rossini, always one of her favourites. Her waiter's smiling approval of her choice amused her, and she allowed herself to be persuaded into glancing over the wine list and selecting a modest half bottle of a sharp white Burgundy, shaking her head over the red he suggested, explaining that she found it too rich.

'No . . . honestly, I couldn't manage another mouthful,' Kirsty pronounced with regret, waving aside the proffered second helping of Californian strawberries.

Once they realised that she was on her own, the waiters had vied with one another to serve her, and she had entered into the rivalry in a lighthearted way. Despite their evening suits and formal expressions, most of them were only boys, similar in age and outlook to her own friends, and Kirsty had never been tonguetied or embarrassed in the presence of the opposite sex. Curiously enough, despite this, neither had she ever fully experienced passion or desire. Until she left home for drama school her only boy-friend had been the son of close friends of her parents; a traditional boy-and-girl relationship, more that of brother and sister than anything else, although they had exchanged the usual shy kisses and fumbling embraces. Since then Kirsty had had plenty of dates with her fellow drama students and their friends, but there had been no one to make her heart beat faster, or lose her head over.

She wanted to make a success of her career before she even thought about falling in love, she had decided long ago, and once she did fall in love it would be with someone who would be as much a friend as a lover.

Accepting the waiter's suggestion that she drink her coffee in the lounge, Kirsty found herself a seat by the door that led on to the foyer. That way she could observe everything going on around her and yet still remain relatively tucked away herself. Her depression seemed to have lifted, and her normal ebullience restored. Even so, some things still rankled. Like Drew Chalmers' criticisms of her, for instance; criticisms which had blighted her career just as she was taking her first faltering steps. He must have known how inexperienced she was; after all, her small part hardly had the power to make or break the play, and yet he had attacked her with a savagery that still felt unhealed wounds. Her pride and self-worth were badly dented, and worse still, she had been forced to ask herself if she was actually going to be able to make it. Of course other members of the cast had come in for criticism too, but none quite so much as her, she was convinced of it. Perhaps he simply didn't like my face, she thought angrily before dismissing the thought as unlikely; under all the stage make-up she had been wearing he wouldn't have been able to see much of the real her, and she had also been wearing a wig. Common sense told her that a highly acclaimed critic would hardly denounce a member of the acting profession simply because he took an immediate dislike to their physical appearance.

Deep down in her heart of hearts Kirsty knew that she had been miscast, but it hurt to admit that there could be roles for which she lacked the experience, so she concentrated on Drew Chalmers' malicious unfairness in picking specifically on her.

The receptionists changed shifts. The new girl, an attractive blonde, was soon busy dealing with a sudden influx of people, when Kirsty saw a tall, dark-haired man cross the foyer and stand easily at the back of the small crowd.

Whether it was the impatient glance he gave the expensive gold watch strapped to a sinewy wrist, or the air of dark authority with which he surveyed his surroundings, Kirsty didn't know, but, trained to recognise such things, she couldn't mistake the alacrity with which the receptionist dealt with the small queue in order to assist him, turning to him with an appreciative smile and a warm 'Good evening.'

For all that he was casually dressed in narrow dark pants and an obviously expensive cashmere sweater in a warm mulberry shade which enhanced a tan Kirsty suspected had never come from any sunbed, when he spoke it was with a crispness that spoke more of the boardroom than a hotel foyer.

'Drew Chalmers,' Kirsty heard him say in stunned disbelief. 'I'm in Room 107.'

Drew Chalmers here! It was almost as though she had conjured him up out of her thoughts. She studied him covertly. This was Drew Chalmers, the man who had ruined her career? She had visualised him as much older than his apparent thirty years; much less obviously male as well. He didn't look a bit as she had imagined him. She had pictured someone smaller, dapper almost, not this six foot odd of lean masculinity with a shock of thick dark hair and a way of moving that reminded her of a lazy cat. Her coffee completely forgotten, she sat transfixed, listening un-ashamedly as he explained that he was expecting a friend to arrive.

'I have to go out for several minutes,' Kirsty heard him explain. 'But if Miss Travers arrives, please give her my key and ask her to let herself into my suite. Oh, and have the dining room send up a bottle of champagne, will you, we'll order dinner later.'

Miss Travers! That could only be Beverley Travers, the newly divorced wife of an American oil millionaire, and according to the gossip columns Drew Chalmers' constant companion.

When she had first heard him announce himself Kirsty had been curious to know what on earth he could be doing in this remote seaside town. Her upper lip curled faintly disdainfully.

Now she knew. How very trite and predictable! If she ever contemplated having an affair with one anyone she would expect him to show far more originally than simply to book them into a quiet country hotel, no matter how luxurious. She spent a few minutes daydreaming about a country cottage tucked away from the rest of the world and the sort of lover she was rather ashamed of fantasising over. Surely she had gone beyond the stage of dreaming of that sort of encounter? Of being swept off her feet and made love to with a thoroughness that would sweep aside all the barriers of modesty and caution instilled into her by her nature and upbringing.

Looking at Drew Chalmers, Kirsty studied his back resentfully. There he was; oblivious to her presence, to the effect he had had upon her life. How would he feel if it had been his life that had been blighted; his bright hopes destroyed, his future left uncertain and unhappy? A thought suddenly struck her, and her eyes widened in appreciation, a determined evident in them.

She looked again at the broad shoulders. Beverley Travers was a very possessive woman, or so she had read, and there had been murmurs in the Press that Drew Chalmers intended to marry her, but, scared by one divorce, she was apparently in no hurry to take on a second husband. An idea had begun to take shape in Kirsty's mind, egged on by the cocktail and wine she had consumed. What if . . .? But no. . . . What was it he had said about her? That no way could she ever persuade any thinking person that she had the ability to perform credibly as an actress?

Well, she would show him, she decided, suddenly coming to a decision. She would show him just how convincing she could be! He would eat those words before the evening was over. All at once a fierce determination filled her, blotting out all the inner voices of caution warning her against what she was contemplating doing, but Kirsty refused to listen to it.

She saw Drew Chalmers leaving the hotel, and got up herself, hurrying quickly to her room. 107, he had said to the receptionist. That was the number of his room, and all she had to do was find it, and conceal herself somewhere in it— either the balcony or the bathroom, if it was the same design as her room, she decided, her thoughts racing ahead as she quickly improved upon her original idea. Drew Chalmers was plainly expecting his mistress; Kirsty intended to turn that romantic scene into something that potentially had all the elements of a Restoration comedy (or a Whitehall farce!), but only she would be able to appreciate the humour of the situation, when she emerged from Drew's bathroom clad in the silk nightdress Chelsea had brought back for her from the South of France during the summer, and proceeded to enact the part of the dizzy ingénue, caught out in her lover's bedroom. Then they would see who couldn't act convincingly, she thought with a satisfied smile. Of course she would be forced to admit to the truth ultimately, but not before she had had the satisfaction of proving his judgment of her wrong.

Carried away by a deliciously heady sense of

anticipated retribution endorsed by cocktails and wine, she refused to admit to any flaws in her plan, any doubts that it might not work, and totally ignored the tiny voice trying to remind her that impetuosity had ever been one of her faults.

It would just serve him right, she decided rebelliously as she opened her own bedroom door. And she hoped it took him all weekend to make Beverley Travers forgive him. He was an arrogant brute; unfeeling too. He must have known she was barely out of drama school. . . . Her thoughts raced busily on, totally absorbed in her plans.

Conscious of the fact that Beverley Travers could arrive at any minute, she quickly peeled off everything but her bra and briefs and then donned the silk nightdress, pulling over it a thick, fleecy dressing-gown that was really a relic from her schooldays, and which was not likely to raise any eyebrows if she was spotted in the corridor.

As luck would have it, the stairs leading to the floor above where Drew Chalmers' room was situated was deserted. It was too early for anyone to be retiring and too late for people to be coming down for dinner. Kirsty found the room without too much difficulty, biting her lip in sudden vexation as she realised she had no means of getting into it.

Furious with herself and on the verge of abandoning her plan, she was shocked into stiff immobility when she felt someone touch her arm.

Dreading coming face to face with Drew Chalmers, she glanced round, then sagged with relief when she realised it was only the chambermaid.

'You 'ave forgotten the key?' The girl was foreign—Spanish, Kirsty guessed, and obviously sympathetic, from her smile. 'See, I have one. I will let you in.'

Truly the gods were favouring her tonight, Kirsty marvelled as she thanked the girl and stepped into the darkened room.

Only it wasn't a room. It was a suite, and she was just gazing open-mouthed round the luxury of a sitting room furnished in chintz and excellent reproduction furniture, when she heard sounds outside. There was barely time for her to slide into the first door—the bedroom, she deduced from the shadowy shape of the bed—before she heard a key in the lock and the sound of the light switch being flicked.

Someone was moving around outside. Kirsty strained her ears, catching the tinkle of ice and other small sounds, before the light was extinguished and the door firmly closed. Then she remembered hearing Drew Chalmers ordering champagne. Tentatively opening the door, she saw that she had guessed correctly. The dim outline of an ice bucket on the low table glinted faintly in the moonlight seeping through the uncurtained window. She let out her breath in relief. Next time she would be prepared. She would have to be! She only hoped that Beverley Travers didn't take it into her head to wait for Drew Chalmers in his bedroom rather than the sitting room. She wanted Drew Chalmers himself to be there when she announced her presence.

She wanted him to witness exactly how convincing she could be as an actress!

She passed the time waiting for Beverley Travers' arrival in silent study of her shadow-shrouded surroundings. The bedroom and its fittings were typically impersonal; hardly seductive, she would have thought, her body tensing as she heard the sound of a key in the lock, and the light being switched on. She held her breath, praying that Beverley Travers—it could only be her this time, surely?—wouldn't come into the bedroom, and it seemed that luck was with her.

How long would Drew Chalmers be? Not long, she imagined. He had told the receptionist that he wouldn't be. Kirsty could hear Beverley Travers moving around outside, the chink of a bottle against glasses, and then she froze with tension as she heard the outer door open, and Drew Chalmers' cool, faintly cynical voice drawling softly, 'Sorry about that, I wanted to get an evening paper.'

'You're a workaholic!' Beverley Travers' voice was warmly seductive. Keyed up and sensitive to everything happening in the other room, Kirsty could imagine the seductive quality of the smile she could sense in the other woman's voice, the way her eyes would linger on Drew Chalmers' arrogant male face.

'Not while you're around.'

She heard Beverley Travers laugh, and then say, 'And champagne—you're spoiling me!'

'Only because you're worth it.'

The words held an undertone of insincerity, as

though they had been said before, and Beverley Travers obviously caught it too, because she demanded sharply, 'Am I? Are you sure I'm not just another pleasant little diversion, Drew? Because that isn't what I want from you.'

That must surely be her cue, Kirsty thought, smoothing damp palms against her dress. Her appearance now would make a definite impact.

And yet, strangely, she felt curiously reluctant to move; in fact she almost wished she had never decided to come up here in the first place. Scared? an inner voice mocked her. She admitted that she was, and then quickly smothered her fear. No actress worthy of the name never felt any tremor of nervousness waiting in the wings, but the time for waiting was over, now she had to go on stage and prove to Mr High and Mighty Chalmers exactly what calibre of actress she was, before her courage deserted her completely.

Taking a deep breath, she moved towards the door, and then thinking quickly, rumpled the severe neatness of the bedclothes, closing her mind against the intimacies her action suggested. What she was doing was in no way underhand, she told herself stubbornly. After all, Beverley Travers must surely know that she wasn't the only woman in Drew Chalmers' life. He featured regularly enough in the gossip columns for even the blindest fool to be aware that he liked variety. Dismissing from her mind the thought of her mother's disapproval, Kirsty reminded herself that she was simply playing a part; showing Drew Chalmers that when it came to acting she could be convincing. Concentrating completely on her role, she pushed open the door and stood there framed in the light, her lips parting on an astonished 'Oh!' as her eyes rounded in a mixture of dismay and surprise.

CHAPTER TWO

'DREW!' Now Beverley Travers' voice was neither soft nor warm. It held bitter incredulity, icy disdain in the pale blue eyes sweeping over Kirsty's disordered hair and rumpled clothes. 'Drew, who is this?'

'Oh, Drew, I'm so sorry,' Kirsty murmured huskily, cutting across the other woman's acid question, one hand stretched pleadingly towards Drew Chalmers as he stared at her with thunderous disbelief in eyes that were the colour of grey flint.

'What the. . . .'

'Oh, Drew, please don't be angry!' Kirsty had the stage now, and allowed her mouth to droop pathetically, tears filling her eyes, as she glanced pleadingly up at the grim mouth, now pulled into a tight hard line. A shiver of premonition iced its way down her spine as she realised that instead of looking disconcerted and embarrassed he was regarding her with a clinical intensity that warned her that she hadn't caught him as much off his guard as she had expected.

Beverley Travers, however, was reacting exactly as Kirsty had anticipated, her face flushed with anger as she looked from Drew Chalmers' impassive face to Kirsty's tear-stained and pleading one.

'I don't pretend to know exactly what's going

on here, Drew,' she said tightly, picking up her handbag and glaring at Kirsty, 'but next time you invite someone to share a rendezvous with you can I suggest that you check with your diary to make sure you haven't double booked. Oh, and by the way. . . .' she paused in the doorway, her eyes slating Kirsty, before they turned, bitter and icy, to Drew Chalmers, relaxed and apparently totally unmoved by what was happening. 'As they say in the movies, don't call me. As for you . . .' her mouth tightened as she glanced contemptuously at Kirsty, 'I presume you're some casual pick-up Drew made on the way down here. You look the type. Really, Drew,' she added coldly as she prepared to sweep out of the suite, 'you ought to be more careful, especially in these permissive times—these little tarts pick up the most obnoxious social diseases, you know.'

Kirsty winced beneath the venom of her words, unaware of the shocked disbelief in her own eyes as they widened slightly in acknowledgement of the thrust. Events had taken a turn she hadn't expected.

The silence following Beverley Travers' furious exit, and her bitter slamming of the door, was a tangible, nerve-aching void, and it took every ounce of courage Kirsty possessed for her to shake her hair nonchalantly over her shoulder and force a blithe smile as she headed for the door.

'Just a moment.'

She hadn't expected him to simply let her go, of course. Nor had she wanted him to do so. The whole purpose of the exercise was to prove to him that his judgment of her had been wrong, but even so Kirsty had a craven desire to turn tail and flee.

'Who the hell are you, and what do you think you're playing at? Blackmail? If so. . . .'

He was advancing on her with purposeful menace, and for one appalling moment Kirsty's mind went completely blank. The clever little speech she had practised until she was word-perfect eluded her completely and she was left scrabbling humiliatingly for words.

'No . . . no, it was nothing like that,' she managed jerkily, and something in her voice must have convinced him, because he stopped advancing on her and instead lounged back against one of the chairs, his expression intent and searching as he demanded tersely,

'Then what was it like? Some kind of sick joke? Some. . . .'

To her relief she managed to pull herself together for long enough to get her handbag open and remove the small newspaper clipping she always carried around with her.

'Remember this?' she demanded, gathering enough composure to sound almost as terse as he had done himself.

He read the article in silence, handing it back to her.

'That actress,' she said unsteadily 'the one you said would make an excellent typist—that was her first role, *my* first role,' she threw at him with bitter passion. 'And I lost it, because of that review, because of you. . . .'

He listened to her in complete and unmoving

silence, unnerving her with his cool scrutiny, his apparent ability to remain unaffected by what had happened.

'And so?'

'And so I decided to prove to you just how convincing an actress I could be,' she told him triumphantly. 'Certainly convincing enough for your mistress!'

'By relying on circumstances rather than ability,' he told her cruelly. 'Effective, but by no means convincing.' His eyes narrowed as he studied her, slowly assessing the tumbled curls and gamine features. 'I still stand by what I said—you weren't right for that part, and you didn't have the ability to make yourself right for it.'

His calm words astounded Kirsty. She had expected him to be furious with her, to rant and rave while *she* remained cool and aloof, and yet somehow he seemed to have turned the tables on her, by reminding her that she had used circumstances rather than ability to convince Beverley Travers that they were lovers. Impotent anger prompted her to demand rashly, 'Do you get some sort of kick out of destroying people, out of ruining their lives . . .?'

'Don't be ridiculous!' The emotionless words silenced her. 'I'm a critic, doing my job, not some sort of a crank on an ego trip. I leave that to the acting profession,' he jibed mockingly. 'Thank God they don't all have your vengeful tendencies! You've been reading too much Shakespeare.' His expression changed suddenly, thick dark lashes veiling his eyes from Kirsty, as he frowned, apparently deep in thought. Now was her chance to leave, Kirsty decided, inching towards the door. She had almost reached it when he moved, reaching it before her to lean against it, his expression cruelly mocking and infinitely dangerous as he asked softly, 'Going somewhere?'

'To my room.' She had intended to sound calmly serene, but even to her own ears her voice had a distinct wobble.

'After depriving me of the company of my—er—mistress, was the rather antiquated term you used, I believe? Oh no, my dear,' he drawled with a soft menace that drove the colour from Kirsty's face. 'In view of what you've just done, I think it's only fair that you make some sort of reparation, don't you?'

He looked so calm and controlled, standing there, flint-grey eyes surveying her mockingly, hands in the pockets of the immaculately cut dark trousers, a leashed power about him that warned her that this was no idle threat, despite the enormity of his words. She licked her lips nervously, trying to meet his ironic gaze with a look equally cool and failing miserably, her protesting, 'I don't know what you mean,' sounding more fearful than firm.

'No? You're lying—but,' he told her in an exceedingly dry tone, 'I'm beginning to think you're right—you are a better actress than I supposed. Come on,' he told her in a hard voice. 'You know exactly what I mean. You've deprived me of a bed partner for the night, to put the matter in its crudest terms, and that being the case I think it only fair that you take her place.'

He was mad! Kirsty thought, searching desperately for some means of escaping the suite that didn't necessitate getting any closer than she already was to that lean, coiled, masculine body, taut with a suppressed violence she was only now beginning to become aware of, so easily had he masked it with his laconic stance and coolly controlled face.

'You can't mean that!' she protested piteously, knowing even as she spoke that it was useless. He had meant it. The sharp flintiness of his glance told her that, the hard implacability of his mouth, and the way it lifted mockingly as he stared down into her flushed and frightened features.

'Amazing!' he taunted at last. 'What a pity I'm your sole audience. That was almost worthy of an Oscar; pity there aren't any parts for distracted innocents any more, you'd fill the bill to a T.'

'Please . . .' Kirsty had gone beyond reasoning, the dark urgency in her eyes unknowingly piteous as she stared up at him.

'Please what?' Drew mocked. 'Throw a crust to the starving orphan? No way,' he added in a much harder voice. 'No one asked you to force your way in here, or act that cute little number you just played. How old are you?' he demanded curtly. 'Eighteen—nineteen? As spoiled as they come; used to widening those big brown eyes and having men drown in them, I don't doubt. Well, it takes more than limpid eyes and a few tears to fool me! If you learn nothing else from this episode, at least you'll learn not to start what you can't finish.'

'You can't mean this!' Kirsty protested, her throat closing in horrified realisation that he did, and that all the pleas in the world weren't going to move him. He was made of solid granite, completely unfeeling, as cold as Arctic ice, impregnable. He must be to even contemplate taking her in place of Beverley Travers. She shuddered, shock taking the last remnants of colour from her face, her mouth drooping, as she sought desperately for some way of convincing him to change his mind. 'You don't even know me. . . .' she managed at last, hating herself for the childish protest, when he laughed—an unexpectedly warm sound, his mouth curling upwards, tiny creases fanning out from his eyes.

'Since when has that been a bar to physical satisfaction?' he asked her coolly. 'Don't tell me you've never heard of instant attraction—love at first sight?'

He was taunting her now, and she hated him for it, her hands curling impotently into her palms as she searched for some stinging retort, something cutting enough to get him away from that door long enough for her to get through it. Too late now to regret her impulsive action, and wish she had never set eyes on him. Too late by far, she acknowledged as the look in his eyes told her he had read her mind and had no intention of letting her get within a yard of the suite door.

'You can't want me,' she burst out childishly at last. 'You love Beverley Travers!'

'But because of you she walked out of here,' he reminded her cruelly, 'and as for not wanting you. . . .'

Kirsty's skin burned as his glance slid slowly over her body, narrowing with devastating explicitness on the softly rounded swell of her breasts, before pinning her to the spot where she stood. 'I'm a man,' he told her softly, 'and you've got an extremely sexy body. Just thank your lucky stars that I don't go in for physical violence—because after what you've done tonight, there isn't a court in the land that wouldn't acquit me of whatever charge you choose to bring against me.' His eyes rested contemptuously on the tangled silky curls she had so deliberately disordered. His mute assessment disturbed her.

'Very effective,' he drawled at last, 'but I'll reserve judgment until I've seen you after I've made love to you.'

'Made love!' Kirsty injected as much scorn as she could into the two words. 'Don't you mean raped me, because I certainly won't. . . .'

'Won't what?' Drew Chalmers asked silkily, levering himself off the door, and walking towards her with a steely determination that made her turn and flee blindly in the opposite direction, not caring that it led only to the bedroom of the suite. 'Respond to me?'

His long legs outpaced her easily, and the breath left her body on a pained gasp as he reached for her, lifting her off her feet, the impotent thud of her small fists against the powerful muscles of his chest hurting her more than it did him.

He carried her as though she weighed no more than a small child, kicking the bedroom door closed behind him, the expression in his eyes as he surveyed the rumpled disorder of his bed making her blood run cold.

'I think,' he told her with icy cold clarity, 'that on this occasion we'll dispense with the champagne and get on with the matter in hand, don't you?'

It came to Kirsty then that behind the cool façade, molten anger boiled and that he meant to degrade and punish her, and that what was going to happen to her had nothing to do with a man satisfying his physical desire for another woman and everything to do with a particularly cruel and degrading form of revenge, and all the fighting spirit drained out of her, a suffocating sense of helpless inevitability overwhelming her.

She was dimly aware of Drew Chalmers dropping her ungently on the bed, and then locking the door, before he came towards her.

'How did you know I would be here tonight?' he asked casually, as the bed depressed under his lean length, the fine fabric of his pants brushing against the silky slenderness of her legs.

'I didn't.' Kirsty recoiled instinctively from the intimate contact with his body, tensing as his gaze narrowed on the pale triangle of her face.

'You're overdoing things,' he warned her softly. 'And it won't work. That frightened virgin act went out years ago—if it was ever in,' he added cynically. 'You're a fraud and a cheat,' he added softly. 'You made damned sure you could use circumstances to suit your own ends and did so without a qualm, but when the tables are turned you don't want to take the nasty medicine, do you? Well, little girl, it's high time someone showed you that sometimes you have to be forced to take it for your own good!'

It was useless trying to tell him that she had had second thoughts the moment she entered the bedroom of his suite, or that she had, in Shakespearean terms, decided upon her plan of action in a mood best described as 'pot-valiant'. Now, when the effects of the wine and cocktail had completely worn off she lay rigid with terror on the bed, unable to decide what was worse—her present situation or the humiliation of the one she would find herself in when Drew Chalmers inevitably discovered the truth.

What would he say if she told him that she was a virgin? Call her a liar, she decided bitterly, willing the weak tears she could feel blocking her throat not to fall, but once again the hatefully drawling mockery of his voice told her that he had guessed when she turned her head slightly and it was ruthlessly turned back with fingers that gripped her chin unkindly and held it while the moon silvered her face, revealing her expression to him while his was concealed from her.

'Crying? Crocodile tears and very pretty, but alas, completely unconvincing. Do you know what the young innocent you're trying to portray would actually do in your circumstances? Well, she certainly wouldn't simply lie here, all passive resistance and melting tears,' he told her brutally, 'she'd be terrified.'

His brutality broke through the strange calm that had descended on her and she struggled to evade the crushing grip of his fingers on her chin, her eyes darting defiance at him as she stormed bitterly, 'How do you know? Do you make a practice out of brutalising inexperienced virgins? Is that how you get your kicks? Is that. . . .'

Her breath was cut off by the sudden fierce pressure of his mouth, as it moved impatiently over hers, stifling her ability to think, swamping her with a terrifying sensation of panic, of swirling blackness and a bottomless pit into which she was being relentlessly drawn.

The tension held her body stiff with rejection; she gulped in air as his head lifted, arms braced against his chest to push him off.

He was breathing heavily, a dark glitter in his eyes, as he said unevenly, 'The way I get my kicks is by having a warm, responsive woman in my arms, and by God, that's what you're going to be, if I have to spend all night making you respond to me!'

He wanted her to respond to him. Kirsty couldn't understand it, unless it was part of his plan to humiliate her by first arousing her and then rejecting her. She had read about such things, and wondered at them, because so far none of her boy-friends had aroused any feelings in her even approaching such an intensity of feeling, and she was beginning to wonder if they existed only in works of fiction.

'I never will,' she told him stubbornly. 'I hate you!'

'Hatred is akin to love, or had you forgotten?' he mocked her, turning her on to her side, one arm curved round her so that her breasts were pressed against the fine silk of his shirt, the hard contact oddly disturbing.

Suddenly it became difficult to breathe normally. Strange sensations vibrated through her, her senses relaying to her an awareness of him that frightened and alarmed her. She could smell the warm maleness of his skin; feel the hardness of sinew and bone beneath the palms she had pressed against his shoulders to fend him off.

'Why don't you simply relax and enjoy yourself?' The self-assured drawl sent shivers of reaction across skin already far too sensitised to his proximity. The arm constraining her moved, and Kirsty breathed a sigh of relief, suddenly suspended as she felt his fingers tugging at her nightdress.

Her instinctive protest froze on her lips as the dark head bent towards her, cool male lips teasing the soft tendrils of hair curling round her forehead, brushing lightly against her skin and evoking a reaction that made her quiver softly. By the time she realised that Drew had eased her nightdress from her shoulders and it was too late for her to do a thing to prevent him, because whichever way she moved, trying to stop him, he outmanoeuvred her, his sudden harsh, 'Look, if you want me to rip the damn thing off you, just say so,' freezing her into a tense stillness, her protests dying in her throat as the nightdress was tugged downwards over her hips and discarded to lie in a pool of silk on the floor.

No man had ever seen her in only her underwear before, and she was all too conscious of the rounded smoothness of her breasts against the sculptured lace of her satin bra and matching cami-knickers suddenly glaringly provocative, and colour swept her body as she saw that Drew was looking at her, studying the slender lines of her body with an expression in his eyes that made her heart stand still before racing erratically, its jerky, uneven pace catching at her breath.

'Beautiful!' The husky timbre of his voice shivered across her nerve endings, the smoky sensuality darkening his eyes from grey almost to black and making her tremble beneath the explicit appraisal of his glance.

When he bent his head, sweeping aside her hair to touch his lips to her throat, exploring the delicate shape of her ear, Kirsty experienced a small explosion of panic, followed by the undeniable knowledge of her body's physical response to a touch so sure and knowing that she marvelled that she could ever have imagined she could withstand it. The touch of his hands on her bare arms and midriff triggered off tiny pinpricks of pleasure, each one shivering through her, shocking her afresh. He seemed to know exactly where to kiss and touch. Violence she could have withstood, but not this subtle, sensual attack on her senses, this slowly seductive destruction of all her barriers until her breasts ached to know the possession of those skilled male hands, her lips parting involuntarily, as his tongue teased their trembling shape, the skilled stroking of his hands along her body, making her forget what had originally brought her to his suite, her body in the grip of a feverishly mounting desire that both shocked and fascinated the tiny corner of her mind which had managed to stand aloof from his expert assault on her senses.

'That's better,' she heard him mutter approvingly, raw sexuality underlining the words as he deftly unfastened her bra, and added throatily, 'much, much better,' his eyes feasting on the swelling curves he had just exposed.

She should feel shame, but she didn't, Kirsty marvelled. Some wild, wanton part of her she had never dreamed existed positively revelled in the hungry intensity of his gaze, but even so, she wasn't prepared for his husky groan or the sight of the dark head buried against her breasts, his breath ragged and warm against the tender flesh as lean fingers cupped her rounded softness.

'God, but you're beautiful! But you already know that, don't you?'

Kirsty trembled as the coaxing fingers stroked tormentingly over the hard arousal of her nipple, her breathing ragged and shallow at the sensation the sensual caress aroused. Deep down inside her something seemed to be flowering into life, a weak, yielding sensation, curling through her stomach, the hands she had lifted to push Drew away in protest, hesitating until the rough texture of his skin against the acutely sensitised tip of her breast made her fingers curl in mute protest into the softness of his hair, a small cry smothered deep in her throat.

'God, I want you! Want you, Kirsty Stannard,' Drew muttered hoarsely as his tongue touched the flesh his thumb had so recently been tormenting. Kirsty's eyes widened in shock at the exquisite flowering of pleasure his touch evoked, and as though he sensed her feelings, Drew muttered something under his breath, his hand cupping the swollen softness of her before his lips closed gently over the throbbing nipple.

Kirsty closed her eyes, shuddering with the waves of pleasure sweeping her, her whole being given up to concentration on the fierce tide of feeling enveloping her. Small moans of delight trembled past her lips, her whole body shaken with the torrent of sensation. Above her she heard Drew groan savagely, 'Kirsty—my God, what are you trying to do to me? Touch me, for God's sake, and stop driving me mad! Can't you tell how much I want to feel all of you against me?'

Kirsty was beyond thought, beyond reason, swept along on a tide of sensual pleasure; a voyage of discovery which was taking her to a world she had never dreamed existed.

Drew's lips left her breasts to trail burning kisses over her collarbone and against her throat. He had pulled of his shirt and the rough tangle of body hair on his chest scraped arousingly against the tenderness of her skin. In a daze Kirsty was aware of his removing his pants; of the powerful masculinity of his thighs, the taut muscles, beneath skin darkened with the same crisp hairs that covered his chest. She made no demur when he removed the last of her own clothes, trembling slightly beneath the burning intensity of his gaze, experiencing for the first time the piercing tension of desire.

'You're a witch, do you know that?' she heard Drew demand thickly as his hand rested possessively on the narrow bones of her hips. 'A witch, and God help me, I want you!'

Kirsty had forgotten that he had promised to make her want him; that the only reason she was here was punishment, and instead, her body gloried in the heady knowledge that she had aroused him; that he wanted her. Innocent though she was, she knew that much; felt it in the taut control of his muscles, saw it in the dark intensity of his eyes as they studied the pale curves of her body; heard it in the husky imprecations he was muttering under his breath, as his hands swept up and moulded her to him, his mouth buried hotly in hers as her arms tightened instinctively around him, her body on fire with a need to melt against him.

When he lifted his mouth it was merely to mutter hoarsely, 'Kirsty, don't make me wait any longer—I can't, God help me. I don't know what it is about you,' he added ruefully, 'but you seem to have turned me into a raw, uncontrolled boy again.' His hands cupped her face as he turned it up to her own. 'Forget what I said earlier,' he told her roughly 'This isn't for revenge, or punishment, or anything else. It's for me,' he added huskily, 'for the sheer pleasure of feeling you melt against me, for knowing the delight of your body. Love me, Kirsty,' he begged throatily, parting her thighs urgently to slide between them, the heated pressure of his mouth silencing every emotion but the need to respond to the demands of his body.

And yet. . . . The taut masculinity of him was faintly alarming. Her muscles tensed automatically, and Kirsty was aware of him hesitating, checking suddenly, a frown touching his eyes.

He moved against her, almost experimentally, Kirsty thought on a sudden burning wave of embarrassment, and yet it was impossible for her to unlock her inexperienced muscles. Half of her still cried out for fulfilment, but the other half protested that things were moving too far too fast. She felt Drew move away from her, and turned her head, unable to meet his eyes.

'Well now.' She was amazed at how calm and controlled he sounded. 'There are only two reasons for a reaction like that. Either you're frigid—which we both know isn't so—or you're still a virgin. Are you, Kirsty?' he demanded, suddenly grasping her shoulders and turning her round to face him. 'And don't lie to me. Are you?'

'Does it make any difference?' Instead of sounding defiant she sounded merely pathetic. Drew swore and she felt tears sting her eyes. An hour ago she would have welcomed this confrontation, welcomed the opportunity to throw her innocence down between them like a gauntlet, but now she felt curiously bereft of the warmth of his body, there was an ache in the pit of her stomach that left her restless and unappeased, and humiliation lay across her mind like a brand because she had betrayed her inexperience so easily, *after* succumbing so completely to his touch.

'I suppose I should have known,' he continued in evident disgust. 'Only a fool or a complete innocent would have pulled a stunt like that in the first place.' He pushed impatient fingers through his hair and reached for her clothes.

'Here, put these on,' he commanded curtly, cursing softly when her fingers trembled over the slips of silk, turning her round while he fastened the clip of her bra, dressing her with the ruthless efficiency he might have applied to a child, his mouth a thin line as he demanded,

'Didn't it ever occur to you what might happen? No, don't bother answering that,' he continued in a harsh voice. 'It's plain your experience of frustrated males is nil.'

He made her sound like a child, Kirsty thought tiredly, and yet only such a short time before he had been all too prepared to consider her a woman. . . .

'Well, perhaps next time you'll think before you act,' he was saying, much like a schoolteacher to a backward pupil, and fresh humiliation seared her. What must he think of her?

'Here!'

He passed her the old dressing gown she had discarded earlier, and while she struggled into it with trembling fingers, Kirsty was aware of him moving about, dressing swiftly.

'Are you staying at the hotel?'

All she could manage was a nod.

'Okay, I'll walk you back to your room. You look as though you could do with a stiff drink first,' Drew added unflatteringly as he switched on the bedside lamp flooding the room with soft colour.

'Bit off more than you bargained for, didn't you? Just out of interest, how far were you prepared to let me go before you finally stopped me, or were you simply looking on it as a good way of broadening your experience?'

Kirsty turned away, but not before he had seen the betraying sheen of tears in her eyes. There was a small explosion of sound and then suddenly his hands were on her shoulders, his voice harsh as he demanded bitingly, 'You little fool, don't you realise how close you came to being raped? Has no one ever told you just how damned hard it is for a man to stop when he's as aroused as you'd got me? The experience might be lacking, but the equipment's there all right,' he added sardonically, watching the colour run up under her skin. 'But next time you feel like experimenting pick on someone your own size.'

'I wasn't,' Kirsty managed on a dignified whisper. 'It was your idea to . . . to. . . .'

'Make love to you?' Drew supplied. 'So it was, but it takes two, you realise, and the kind of response I was getting from you. . . .' He broke off suddenly and looked at her. 'It was the first time, wasn't it?' he asked expressionlessly, watching her with cool grey eyes that seemed to see right inside her head and make it impossible for her to lie.

Her, 'Yes,' sounded hunted and strangled, and Kirsty couldn't meet his eyes, sure that she would read amused contempt there for her inexperience.

'And at a guess you forgot what you were doing in my arms in the first place.' He seemed to be speaking more to himself than her, and Kirsty was surprised to hear him add dryly, 'Quite a salutary experience—for both of us. You're a very desirable young lady, Kirsty Stannard, a very dynamic package, but in future, unless you want to lose that innocence very quickly, stop trying to pretend you're something you aren't. Have you any idea how close I came to taking you?' he asked softly, with no mercy for the quick flood of colour under her skin.

'Come on,' he said at last. 'I'll walk you to your room, and order a drink from the kitchens for you—something to help you sleep.'

'I'm not a child!' Kirsty told him indignantly. 'I. . . .'

'Save it,' she was advised with dry impatience, followed by a curt, 'What the devil are your parents thinking about, letting a baby like you loose on the streets?'

'I'm not a baby,' Kirsty stormed back at him. 'I'm twenty!'

'A very great age,' Drew taunted. 'But I'm talking about experience, not age, little girl, and when it comes to the former. . . .'

'I'm simply not in the same league as the Beverley Travers of this world,' Kirsty supplied with a bitterness that surprised her.

'Nowhere near it,' Drew assured her mockingly. 'Now come on, let's get you tucked up in your little bed, before you go and drive some other unsuspecting male half crazy!'

Those minutes in his arms when he had wanted her so much that he had been tense with the effort on containing it might never have been. All at once she had been relegated to the role of child, and irrationally she resented it.

In the end Drew left her outside her room, but long after he had gone Kirsty lay awake reliving those emotions she had experienced in his arms, shivering at the knowledge that it had taken him to arouse them. A pure fluke, she assured herself, nothing more, and thank God she would never have to set eyes on him again. She didn't think she could endure the humiliation. Bad enough if he had actually 'raped' her, as he described it, but in some ways worse to have been found out and rejected on the grounds of her innocence; to have fallen short of his requirements in a woman and be dismissed merely as a foolish child.

She had heard other people describing virginity as a 'turn-off', but this was the first time she had come across concrete evidence of the fact. Drew had desired her, she knew that, but the moment he realised that she was still a virgin his desire had gone. Kirsty writhed in a torment of mortified chagrin; somehow the swift death of his desire made her feel a failure as a woman, a freak almost. What was the matter with her? she asked herself. She ought to be thanking her lucky stars. Self-disgust rose up inside her. What on earth had happened to her belief that physical desire was nothing without love? Why had she responded in the first place? Had perhaps fear released an adrenalin into her blood which had led to that warm, yielding tide of desire? That must be the explanation. Feeling happier, Kirsty closed her eyes. If she was honest she was forced to admit that she had been foolish enough to go to Drew Chalmers' suite, but having done so and endured the after-effects, all she wanted to do now was to put the whole affair behind her, and forget about the incident completely. She could only thank her lucky stars that her path and Drew's were hardly likely to cross again!

CHAPTER THREE

WAS she dreaming, Kirsty wondered, waiting in the wings for her turn to read, or was she actually here in Yorkshire, ready to go on stage for her first rehearsal as Hero, in *Much Ado About Nothing*?

She pinched herself just to make sure, reassured by the tingling pain in her arm. So much had happened in such a short period of time; first the failure of her previous play—not exactly unexpected—and then the phone call from her agent, Eve, in London telling her that she was to present herself in Ousebridge in Yorkshire for an audition for the part of Hero.

What had totally floored them both was that the director and producer Simon Bailey had specifically asked for her. He had heard that she might make an excellent Hero from a friend who had seen her on stage, he had told Kirsty with a smile when she had commented a little breathlessly on her good fortune in being invited to audition. Parts like Hero did not come the way of struggling young actresses very often, especially with such prestigious companies as the Ousebridge Players.

'That was excellent, Kirsty,' Simon approved as she came off stage. 'You're beginning to get the idea. Like I said, I want to get right away from the hackneyed image of Hero, and instil something a little different.'

Her head in the clouds, Kirsty hurried down to the communal dressing room, her mind already on the letter she would write to her parents when she returned to her hotel.

They had been thrilled for her, of course, and her mother had even gone so far as to loan Kirsty her precious Mini for the duration of her stay in Yorkshire.

'Don't forget about the party tomorrow, will you, Kirsty?' Cherry Rivers, the A.S.M., called as she hurried past the open door. 'All the rest of the cast will be there!'

Simon had already invited her to the get-together party he and his wife were holding for the cast of *Much Ado*. As he had explained to Kirsty when he initially auditioned her, the Ousebridge had only a very small nucleus of permanent actors, preferring to audition afresh for each play, and because of their excellent reputation they were normally able to obtain some of the more glittering stars of the theatrical world to play their leading roles. For *Much Ado*, they were lucky enough to have a world-famous actress to play Beatrice. Kirsty had seen her once in the West End, and was rather overwhelmed at the thought of appearing in the same production as such a well-known personality.

She had already met the small nucleus of permanent cast, one of whom was Simon Bailey's wife. She, she explained cheerfully to Kirsty, was unable to take part in the current production owing to the fact that she was expecting their second child, which was one of the reasons they needed Kirsty.

'She had a miscarriage eighteen months ago,' Cherry had told Kirsty later, 'and because of that Simon is insisting she takes things easy this time—I don't think she minds, though, she's always said she prefers being a wife and mother to the stage. I can see you doing the same thing,' she had confounded Kirsty by telling her. 'You don't have that hungry, driving look one always associates with the ones that make it to the top. Don't look so upset,' she had consoled her. 'Absolute dedication, heart, soul and body, isn't always a good thing.'

Kirsty had liked Cherry right from the start and she had proved a fund of information about the Ousebridge Players and the people connected with them. And at least someone had thought her acting ability worthy of note and recommendation, even if Drew Chalmers did not. Drew Chalmers! Why on earth had she had to think about him? She loathed the man, but he had developed a disconcerting habit of stealing into her mind when she was least expecting it. Had she been less honest with herself she might have been able to delude herself into believing that what had happened in his suite had come unpleasantly close to rape, but her scrupulous inborn honesty wouldn't let her off so lightly. However unwittingly and briefly, she *had* participated.

Her fingers curled into her palms as she left the theatre and headed for her Mini, mentally reliving the turbulence of those moments when Drew had touched her body; the excitingly sensual roughness of his body hair against her skin; the skilled possession of his kiss.

'No!' She shook her head vigorously, as though by doing so she could dislodge the persistent memories, but they clung as tenaciously as steel sutured cobwebs.

She had been at Ousebridge just over a week now—long enough for her to have put Drew Chalmers completely out of her mind, but instead. . . .

Just let him wait, she thought wrathfully, waiting for an opportunity to join the stream of traffic along the High Street, just let him wait; she would show him!

In the short space of time it took to drive from the theatre to the quiet hotel where she was staying she became lost in a delightful daydream composed of glowing tributes to her interpretation of Hero; somehow—and the exact accomplishment of it was still very hazy—Drew Chalmers would be in the forefront of this worshipping crowd, full of apologies for previously misjudging her; and ready to tell the world of his folly in doing so.

She came down to earth with a bump when another irate motorist blew his horn at her and she realised that he was flashing her to let her go. How crazy could she get? she asked herself wryly as she drove on. The day Drew Chalmers had a good word to say about her would never dawn.

Her evenings had developed into a similar pattern since her arrival in Yorkshire. After dinner she either retired to the hotel lounge and watched television and read, or she went to her room and studied her part. Tonight she had decided to do the latter, but she had barely done little more than read through the first two acts before she started to wonder who could have recommended her in glowing enough terms to Simon Bailey to make him audition her.

That she had been fantastically lucky was in no doubt. She knew from Cherry that she was the youngest and most inexperienced member of the cast; and although she knew that parts were obtained by word of mouth references, she hadn't thought she numbered anyone amongst her acquaintances influential enough to get her considered for such a prestigious company.

She put the typed sheets on one side, and opened her wardrobe on impulse, wondering what on earth she was going to wear to the party.

The Baileys had invited the entire cast, plus several local dignitaries; financiers and friends.

'You'll enjoy it,' Cherry had assured her when it was first mentioned. 'It's a regular thing, and like you I was terrified the first time I was invited to one when I joined the company two years ago. You sometimes get a certain amount of bitching,' she had added, 'but then of course that's the theatre for you!'

In the end Kirsty elected to wear a silk jersey dress in a rich cinnamon shade which had been a gift from Chelsea. Her aunt had brought it for herself and then decided that the colour did nothing for her, so Kirsty had inherited it.

It was far more sophisticated than the clothes she normally wore, but she was glad she had chosen it when the front door of the Baileys' substantial foursquare Georgian house opened to her knock and she saw how glamorously the other female guests were dressed.

'You made it—I'm so glad!' Helen Bailey said warmly as she took her coat and led the way up an attractive flight of stairs to what was obviously a spare bedroom, gesturing to Kirsty to make use of the dressing table and full-length mirror as she hung her coat in the spacious cupboard. 'Simon tells me he's got high hopes of your Hero,' she added with a smile, breaking off to excuse herself as the doorbell pealed again. 'Can you find your own way down?' she asked hesitantly. 'Or. . . .'

'I'll be fine,' Kirsty assured her, not wanting to admit that without her hostess's supportive presence she felt more like hiding herself away in the bedroom than going back downstairs. She hadn't felt so alien and unsure of herself since secondary school. Her initial euphoric delight at getting the role had worn off during the night and she had woken up this morning seized with the conviction that she simply wasn't up to the role of Hero, and never, ever would be.

There was a crowd of people milling about in the hall when she went downstairs, and she was just hesitating on the stairs when Cherry suddenly pounced on her, her eyebrows rising a little as she studied her slowly.

'Wow, that's some dress,' she pronounced at last. 'And not exactly chain-store either!'

It was impossible for Kirsty to be offended by her frank manner, and she explained lightly that it had been given to her.

'Lucky you—which reminds me, another piece of luck for you. Simon asked me to enquire about lodgings for you, and I think I've found you some, but come and meet the others first, we'll talk about it later.'

She plunged into the crowd, leaving Kirsty no option but to follow her, hoping that she had indeed found her somewhere to stay. Pleasant though the hotel was, it was proving a drain on her resources that she could ill afford.

She was introduced to so many people in such quick succession that she was convinced she would never remember their names. However, she did have an excellent memory for faces, and she just prayed that when she did meet them again at rehearsals they would reintroduce themselves.

'Come and meet Clive Richmond, who's playing Borachio,' Cherry instructed. 'But be warned—he's something of a flirt.'

'Who, me?' Clive expostulated in mock-hurt accents. 'Don't listen to her, Kirsty, it's all lies!'

They exchanged cheerful banter for several minutes, the sensation of being the only outsider at the party gradually leaving her as Kirsty joined in the conversation, and then allowed Cherry to detach her from Clive in order to introduce her to some of the others.

'Exhausting, but necessary,' she whispered to Kirsty at one point. 'At least when you go home you'll be able to say you've spoken to everyone. . . . Oh yes, and before I forget—about your lodgings. They're with Mrs Cummings. She's a widow—lives alone in a large old semi about a mile away from the theatre. She's just had the upstairs converted into two self-contained bedsits. One of them she's going to let to her niece who works in York, but she's offered to let you have the other if you want it. The rent is very reasonable. She doesn't provide meals, but I've seen the flat—there's a marvellous purpose-built kitchen affair that can be partitioned off from the rest of the room. Shall I tell her you're interested?'

'Please. It sounds great!'

'Well, now that that's settled and you've met almost everyone, I suggest we give our feet a rest and find something to eat and drink,' Cherry suggested practically. 'Helen always puts on a superb spread. She and Simon make a good couple, don't they?'

Agreeing, Kirsty followed her through the crowd. Cherry seemed to know her way round, and half an hour later, her plate filled with all manner of tempting bites, Kirsty sank gratefully into a chair next to Cherry, listening to her chattering about the other guests.

It was apparent that she knew most of them quite well; her comments were shrewd and funny, but never deliberately malicious. Only when Clive was mentioned did her voice change slightly. A flirt, she had called him, and although she would bear her warning in mind, Kirsty resolved to reserve judgment until she knew him a little better, because initially she had quite liked him.

'Here comes our leading lady and her husband,' Cherry announced suddenly. 'She's just finished filming a new series for television—Simon was jolly lucky to get her.'

Peering over her shoulder, Kirsty caught a glimpse of the famous actress through the crowd surrounding her.

'I've heard she's isn't all sweetness and light with the lower orders,' Cherry warned her. 'Oh no—and just look who she's brought with her!' she groaned suddenly as the crowd parted.

Craning her neck, Kirsty did, paling as she recognised the beautiful mask-like features of Beverley Travers. Of all the bad luck!

'They went to school together,' Cherry chattered on, blithely oblivious to Kirsty's consternation. 'Bosom friends and all that, although you can bet your bottom dollar it isn't friendship that's brought her here tonight.' She stressed the word 'friendship', and grimaced slightly, but Kirsty was too dismayed by Beverley Travers' unexpected appearance to question her further. Later she was to wish she had done, but by then it was too late. Far too late.

The Baileys' house was a comfortable size, and the drawing room carpet had been rolled back so that people could dance. An attractive teenager Cherry referred to as 'Jim—he helps out after school and is a fantastic scenery shifter,' seemed to be in charge of the hi-fi. Several couples were already dancing when Clive approached Kirsty and asked her to dance with him. Cherry was already dancing and Kirsty had no hesitation in accepting his invitation. She suspected that Cherry was quite right when she described him as a 'flirt' and moreover that she had been tactfully advising her of that fact, nevertheless he was good company, attractive and good fun, and

she enjoyed the fifteen minutes or so she spent
with him, and returned to her chair and her plate
of food slightly breathless, warm colour tinging
her clear skin.

'Where do you find the energy?' Helen asked
her. 'I envy you! Still, once junior arrives
safely. . . .' she patted her stomach and smiled,
and mindful of what she had been told Kirsty
wondered if perhaps Helen ought to be resting
rather than tiring herself out entertaining them
all. Something of her feelings obviously showed
in her face, because Helen laughed. 'Don't
worry,' she told her. 'I'm not as delicate as Simon
likes to pretend—I've always been a semi-
reluctant actress. Going on stage is something I
always have to psyche myself up to, and it's the
strain of that rather than any physical tiredness I
have to avoid. That's why I'm not taking part in
Much Ado.

'Oh, here's Drew at last,' she exclaimed
suddenly, a delightful smile illuminating her
features. 'Have you known him long?'

Drew? Did Helen mean Drew Chalmers?
Kirsty stared at her in appalled disbelief.

'Drew Chalmers?' she questioned huskily.
'But. . . .'

'You knew he was hoping to come, of course?'
Helen was frowning now, obviously perplexed by
Kirsty's attitude. 'Of course, as Simon's partner
Drew does try to come up here as often as he can,
but as you will know, he has so many other
business interests.'

Drew Chalmers was Simon's partner—of all
the appalling coincidences! Kirsty swallowed and

tried to conceal her dismay. Out of the corner of her eye she glimpsed the familiar male outline of him; how could she ever forget it, it was engraved on her heart, but this was the last place she had expected to see him. She could only pray that Helen would go and give her an opportunity to escape before Drew spotted her.

She was just starting to inch away when Helen raised her hand and beckoned Drew over. Kirsty felt as though she wanted the ground to open up and swallow her, but it was no use telling Helen that she was the last person Drew would want to meet socially.

She was so engrossed in her own thoughts that she didn't hear the beginning of Helen's next sentence, merely catching the tail-end of it, but what she did hear was enough to widen her eyes in disbelief, her mind reeling with shock.

'You mean Drew recommended me for Hero?' she exclaimed in a shaken voice. 'But he'd never do that, he. . . .'

'I can assure you that he did,' Helen confirmed merrily. 'I must admit that at first Simon had doubts—after all, you're very young, very inexperienced, but he has a good deal of faith in Drew's judgment—it's always proved sound in the past, although this is the first time he's ever actively recommended such a relative unknown— of course, he does see much more of what's going on in the theatre through his work as a critic.'

Kirsty was still trying to assimilate the shock of firstly seeing Drew here—the last place she had expected him to be—and secondly, and perhaps worse, his involvement with the Ousebridge

Players and his recommendation of her to Simon. It was something she was finding it impossible to come to terms with.

Why on earth had he recommended her? It was something she simply could not understand. And what must the rest of the cast think? She writhed mentally in horror; they must know how she had got the part, did they think that she had asked Drew to intercede on her behalf? It certainly wouldn't be the first time something like that had happened, but even if she was able to wield such influence she would never, never do so. If she was to succeed she wanted to do so on her own merits. It was totally abhorrent to her to think that Drew Chalmers had been responsible for her getting the part. And yet only a handful of hours before she had been mentally thanking her unknown champion, making a vow not to let the company down. But that was before she had realised that Drew Chalmers was the one who had recommended her. Why? Because of what had happened in Winton?

She moved slightly, stifling a gasp as she realised that he was looking directly at her, freezing like a tiny trapped animal caught in the mesmerising glare of a predator's gaze. He moved, lean and graceful in formal evening clothes; a man who automatically drew the eye of those who saw him, his predatory, tigerish stalk carrying him through the crowd that parted automatically for him. He was smiling at her, tiny lines fanning out from the corners of his eyes, his mouth quirked in amusement, and Kirsty felt the resentment boil up inside her. How dared he

take it for granted that she would be grateful for
his intervention—and that was what his smile
suggested. Didn't he realise that she would far
rather have succeeded on her own merits? And
why had he done it? Not simply out of charity. A
terrible thought struck her. He had been furious,
she knew, at the trick she had played on him.
Could this be his way of taking revenge; getting
her a part that she herself suspected might be
beyond her and then sitting back to watch her
fail, before reminding her of his earlier judgment—proved correct by yet another failure. She
darted a quick glance at the impassive features.
Someone was talking to him and he was giving
them his whole attention, yet it was impossible to
read anything in his face. He was a man who was
adept at concealing his real feelings, and yet they
would run deep, Kirsty sensed that instinctively.
She had played with those feelings as carelessly as
a child might a box of matches, without realising
the danger, until it was too late. Was Drew
capable of acting in such a cold-blooded fashion?
Her instincts gave her an unequivocal 'yes', and
she shivered suddenly, causing Helen to frown in
concern and ask if she was cold.

Reassuring her hostess, Kirsty was just about
to excuse herself when Beverley Travers suddenly
materialised at Drew's side, her eyes narrowing
in recognition and dislike as she spotted Kirsty.

'Darling!' she trilled in a clear carrying voice,
polished fingernails bright spots of crimson
against the silky fabric of Drew's shirt. 'Isn't that
your little bedmate over there?' She was looking
directly at Kirsty and there was no way that she

or anyone else could mistake the remark or the look that accompanied it.

Kristy coloured to the roots of her hair, paling just as suddenly, conscious of Helen's small gasp, and her protective hand on her arm; of Drew's sudden frown, his grey gaze impaling her where she stood.

Everybody in the room seemed to be looking at her. They had all heard Beverley Travers' deliberately malicious remark. Kirsty had a cowardly impulse to turn and run—and then Drew stepped forward, smiling lazily at Helen. Kirsty couldn't look at him, so the sudden shock of his fingers curling round her arm was even greater, his breath stirring the faint tendrils of hair on her forehead as she heard him saying lazily over her head, 'Helen, will you forgive us if I take advantage of your party to make a rather special announcement?'

Helen was laughing, and as Drew hadn't lowered his voice at all, but had spoken in a cool but quite discernible tone, people standing within earshot had forgotten their own conversations in favour of listening to his.

This was it, Kirsty thought fatalistically. Having recommended her to the Baileys, he was now going to announce that he had changed his mind and why. She wanted to turn and run, melt away—anything to escape the dénouement she knew was to come. As though he sensed her desire to escape Drew's grip on her arm tightened, the touch of those hard, lean fingers causing curious sensations to radiate outwards, from the spot where the careless stroke of the ball of his thumb over her skin sent frissons of awareness along her nerve endings. The caress was automatic and oddly soothing, nevertheless she was tense, anticipating with every second hearing his dry criticisms of her ability.

'Well, darling?' The words were anything but dry; and so huskily sensual that at first Kirsty didn't realise he was addressing them to her; and in fact would have gone on oblivious to the fact that he was addressing her if Helen hadn't smiled conspiratorially at them and murmured, 'I'll leave you to it.'

To what? Kirsty wondered dumbfounded, unable to think beyond the unreality of having Drew look at her with a tenderness that brought a strange lump to her throat, her mouth painfully dry as he turned her unresisting body to face him, his lips against her temple as he murmured quite audibly, 'Shall I tell them, then?'

The smile he gave her as he kissed her lightly and then held her slightly away bemused her with its teasing warmth.

'Tell them what?' she was about to demand croakily, when Beverley Travers, obviously as much in the dark as Kirsty was herself, pushed past her friends to confront Drew, anger flashing in her eyes as she insisted, 'I want to know what's going on! First I discover this . . . this . . . person in your suite, and now. . . .'

'Then I'll tell you.' Drew spoke quite calmly, but the look in his eyes would have frozen molten lava at a thousand feet and Kirsty was glad that she was not on the receiving end of it. 'Kirsty and I are engaged.'

Kirsty didn't know which of them was the more stunned. She rather thought it was her. Beverley Travers' shock, although painfully evident, was quickly masked, a sneer quickly curling her mouth as she said cuttingly, 'Clever little girl, but it won't last.' And then she was gone, turning on her heel and stalking through the crowd of people pressing in on them offering congratulations, masking their evident curiosity, chattering blithely about wedding dates and dark horses.

Kirsty stood it as long as she could and then suddenly could bear it no more. She longed for peace and quiet; to escape somewhere where she could come to terms with Drew's shock announcement. Why had he done it? To punish Beverley Travers for walking out on him that night in his suite? Surely that must be the answer. In another man she might have thought his action born of some quixotic and chivalrous desire to protect her good name—after all, as both of them knew, Beverley Travers' implication had had no true base, but then Beverley hadn't known that. Nor did she know how close it had come to being true. Kirsty's face flamed as she remembered that Drew had been the one to draw back, the one to call a halt.

'Drew, Kirsty looks positively faint!'

Helen's concerned tones cut through the fog of bewilderment enshrouding her, and the next thing she knew Drew was marshalling her towards some chairs, his murmured, 'Now don't you dare run away!' holding enough of a threat to send her nervous system into a frantic overdrive.

Not that she was given any opportunity to flee, much as she would have liked to. No sooner had Drew left her to go and get her a drink than she was surrounded by avid questioners. When had she and Drew met? How long had they known one another? etc., etc. Cherry had just reached her when she saw Drew returning with a tall, frosted glass.

'Well, well, you kept that a dark secret,' Cherry commented. 'I don't suppose you'll need Mrs Cummings' bedsit now.' When Kirsty looked uncomprehendingly at her, she added kindly, 'Drew won't want you living alone when you could share his house. He bought it when he originally invested in the theatre, and although he can't spend as much time up here as Simon and Helen would like he keeps on the house for those occasions when he can.

Drew had invested in the theatre! Kirsty's mouth fell open, and then suddenly the full meaning of Cherry's comment became plain and colour surged into her too pale face. Fortunately, before Cherry could comment, Drew had reached them and was placing her glass on a small table he had commandeered.

'What have you been saying to Kirsty to make her go that colour?' he demanded of Cherry in a friendly manner, one arm draped casually round Kirsty's shoulders, as he drew her down towards his shoulder.

Really, the man had missed his true calling, Kirsty thought bitterly. He was a consummate actor, currently engaged on giving his all to the role of newly engaged male, but why? Had she been right? Was it because of Beverley Travers?

'I was just saying she wouldn't need Mrs Cummings' bedsit now that the pair of you had announced your engagement. She'll be living with you.'

Kirsty found it impossible to look at him, which was quite ridiculous. He meant absolutely nothing to her; there was no reason why she should feel the slightest bit of embarrassment, but she did. She felt both embarrassed and confused, without being able to understand why. The mere suggestion of them 'living together' had been enough to remind her of that night in his suite; of how it had felt to have his arms round her, the male warmth of his body covering hers.

'Excellent though your suggestion sounds, somehow I can't see Kirsty agreeing to it.'

Wretched man! Kirsty thought, disbelieving what she was hearing. Drew had managed to inject into his voice a nicely judged blend of regret and acceptance, and she could see that Cherry was completely taken in by it, even before she heard her laugh as she commented,

'Wise girl! You keep him in his place, Kirsty— but you could have told us that this was in the wind, you know,' she added. 'Why didn't you? Helen and Simon would have been delighted. They've been urging him to sample the delights of wedded bliss for years.'

'I wanted to tell them all along,' Drew announced, astounding Kirsty with another barefaced lie, 'but Kirsty had the notion that if they did they'd be bound to take her on, whether they thought she was up to the part or not.'

'While of course, merely having you recommend me to them wasn't moral blackmail at all,' Kirsty scoffed, letting a little of her anger show in her eyes as she turned to face him.

She had forgotten that Cherry was still there until the other girl chuckled, but as always Drew had a ready answer.

'Not the way I look at it,' he agreed. 'I'd already told them I was going to spend part of the next six months up here with them—Simon needs a break, he's earned it, and naturally I wanted you with me. I've got it both ways now,' he added with a slow smile. 'Simon tells me you signed the contract yesterday.'

The contract! Kirsty had forgotten about that. Trust Drew with his Machiavellian mind to guess that she had been planning to tell Simon she had changed her mind and to leave Ousebridge just as quickly as she could.

'And you needn't worry about Kirsty not being up to the part,' he told Cherry, further confounding Kirsty. 'If I'd had any doubts on that score, I'd never have recommended her to Simon, love of my life or not.'

It was obvious that Cherry was completely taken in by his pseudo-sincerity, and Kirsty ground her teeth in helpless resentment as the other girl beamed a smile of approval at him.

'How did you two come to meet in the first place?' she questioned. 'I mean, Kirsty here has only just left drama school, and Drew. . . .'

'Is a famed, not to say notorious drama critic, way, way above the likes of struggling unknowns,' Kirsty supplied with saccharine sweetness. 'Well. . . .'

'We met when Kirsty was performing in the
new Alan Forster play,' Drew supplied. 'She had
the part of Myra—and played it abysmally, I
might add,' he went on without batting an eyelid.
'It was the worst piece of miscasting I've ever
had the misfortune to witness.'

'No wonder he felt he had to tie you down with
a contract!' Cherry marvelled. 'He doesn't believe
in pulling his punches, does he?'

Kirsty opened her mouth to speak, to tell
Cherry the truth, but once again Drew forestalled
her, laughter lurking in his eyes as he said
suavely,

'If you'd let me finish, I was going to add that
the director in me couldn't resist the challenge of
finding her the right part—as it happens, two
right parts, the future Mrs Chalmers and Hero—
you see, I'm getting her well trained,' he added
teasingly. 'Hero is perfect wife material, and I
only hope Kirsty takes due note of that fact while
she's playing her!'

Cherry's mirth left Kirsty with no alternative
but to grind her teeth in silent and bitter fury,
and that interlude set the tone for the entire
evening. Wherever she went, whoever she talked
to, Drew was at her side; the perfect fiancé, only
Kirsty aware of how tight his grip of her arm
actually was, of the menace behind the warm
smile. What was he trying to do to her? Or was
she simply a pawn he was using against Beverley
Travers, deeming it a fitting revenge for the trick
she had played on him, using her until he saw fit
to discard her with another grating criticism that
would leave her career in ruins.

The only time she managed to escape him, Helen found her, her face breaking into a delighted smile as she told her again how thrilled she was by the news of their engagement.

'I can understand you wanting to keep quiet about it,' she sympathised, 'but you mustn't think that Simon took you on because of Drew. Good friends and business partners though they are, Simon would never forsake his own standards simply to please Drew, and nor would Drew expect him too. I'm so glad he's found someone like you,' she added simply. 'For a while I feared he was becoming too embittered and cynical—our life can affect you like that. I was dreading hearing that Beverley had managed to snare him. I wouldn't have minded if I thought for a moment that she genuinely loved Drew, but I doubt that she's capable of loving anyone apart from herself. She's intrinsically cold and hostile. I sense it every time I go anywhere near her.' She laughed mischievously, obviously suddenly struck by something. 'I can't wait to see the fireworks when you and Drew have to work together,' she explained. 'I haven't forgotten what it was like when Simon first directed me—fight!' She raised her eyebrows in mock despair. 'It was dreadful— worth it, though,' she added with a grin, 'when we made up afterwards.' She laughed again when she saw Kirsty blush. 'I'd forgotten how young you are,' she said. 'Eighteen—nineteen?'

'Twenty,' Kirsty corrected her, biting her lip when she realised how juvenile the claim sounded.

'Umm, and Drew's thirty—thirty-one soon,'

Helen amended with another grin. 'Ten years between you—a nice age gap, I think. There's eight between Simon and me; just enough to put us in different decades and add a little extra spice to life. I hope you'll be very happy,' she added on a more serious note. 'Oh, and Drew tells me he's taking you to York on Monday to get your ring. He explained that he hadn't had time to talk to your parents yet, and that he'd originally intended not to announce anything until he'd done so. However, in the circumstances I'm sure they'll forgive him. I hope you weren't upset by Beverley's bitchiness. Drew explained to us how she burst in on you, and immediately leapt to the wrong conclusion. He must have been thrilled when you arrived unexpectedly like that—especially when he admitted that he was the one to blame for your quarrel.'

What would Helen say if she were to tell her that everything her precious Drew had said was a pack of lies, and that he had a remarkably inventive imagination? Kirsty wondered bitterly. She was in a cleft stick and he knew it, damn him. As he had already reminded her, she was bound by a legal contract to the company now, and yet if she stayed she would be forced to play along with this ridiculous fictitious 'engagement' until he chose to end it. What did he intend to do? Make her humiliation complete by breaking off their engagement at the same time as he announced that she wasn't capable of playing Hero? It all fitted together so logically, so demoniacally; and she had actually believed someone had recommended her for the part because they believed in her. Oh, if she'd been that sort of female she could have wept!

CHAPTER FOUR

THE evening seemed interminable. Kirsty was all too aware of the sidelong glances she was getting from other members of the cast, burningly conscious of the comments they must be making to one another, and this was borne out when Clive approached her towards the end of the evening, to add his best wishes to everyone else's.

'Quite the dark horse, aren't you,' he said lightly, 'but don't worry about it. At least no one could accuse you of getting the part by virtue of being an old man's darling—the time-honoured way to stage fame—or at least it was, about fifty years ago. For one thing, Drew is far too much of a catch. There'll be more than one pair of jealous green eyes turned in your direction when this becomes public.'

Public! That was something Kirsty hadn't thought of. She must get in touch with her parents, she thought feverishly, and explain. . . . But explain what? She gnawed worriedly at her lip. Oh, why had Drew announced their 'engagement'? He must have known there would be all manner of repercussions and problems. Why couldn't he simply have announced that they were lovers if he had to say anything—it would have had an equally explosive effect and would have been far less messy. How could she explain to her parents? She tried to visualise telling them what had happened at Winton, and the consequent results. They would never understand, she acknowledged unhappily. Chelsea would, but this was one scrape her aunt couldn't get her out of. This was something she had to face alone.

Strangely enough, with that thought formulated and accepted, Kirsty felt as though she had suddenly taken a giant-sized step forward into adulthood.

'You're looking pensive. Ready to leave?'

She hadn't heard Drew come up behind her. When he wanted to, he could move with the stealth of a jungle cat, she decided resentfully.

Even though she was tired and longing for the evening to draw to a close, some spark of contrariness made her say stubbornly, 'No way. Besides, hardly anyone has left yet.'

'Hardly anyone else had just announced their engagement,' Drew reminded her, irony underlining the words. 'They expect us to leave,' he added pointedly. 'They expect that as a newly engaged couple we want to be alone.'

'And whose fault is it that they're going to be disappointed?' Kirsty demanded bitterly. 'Who lied to them, who told them we were engaged when. . . .'

Her angry protests were stifled beneath the hard pressure of his lips. The hands which had been hanging easily at his sides were now gripping her shoulders, the pressure of his mouth forcing her head backwards, and her lips to part so that she could draw in a gasping breath.

'How dare you . . .!' she started to say when she

could speak again, but she wasn't allowed to do more than frame the first two words before Drew's lips were brushing softly against her own again, masking the whispered threat he murmured against her skin, as he warned her not to make a scene in front of the others.

'Then let's go somewhere where I can make one,' Kirsty suggested icily, unaware until he agreed that she had played completely into his hands, and that not only were they leaving the party, they were also leaving it together— something she had already made a promise to herself she wasn't going to allow to happen under any circumstances.

They had to run the gamut of a good deal of ribald comment before they were allowed to escape, and Kirsty's cheeks were flushed a warm pink by the time they emerged into the cool September night.

The nostalgic scent of woodsmoke and autumn hung on the air, a feeling of indefinable sadness that autumn always brought.

Simon and Helen accompanied them outside.

'Oh, you came in your car,' Helen said, frowning, as Kirsty pulled away from Drew and headed for her Mini.

'Like you, she wasn't sure if I could make it,' Drew interrupted smoothly. 'I don't suppose you'd give it a good home overnight?' he added humorously.

'Of course we would,' Helen assured him before Kirsty could so much as open her mouth, 'after all, you've barely had an opportunity yet to celebrate your engagement,' she added with a teasing grin.

'We're not. . . .' We're not engaged, was what Kirsty had been about to say, but once again Drew forestalled her. 'We're very grateful to you both,' he interposed easily. 'Look, darling, my car's right at the bottom of the drive—one of the misfortunes of arriving late—so why don't you stay here with Helen and Simon while I go and collect it. I won't be long.'

Very clever, Kirsty seethed as he walked away. Now she wouldn't be able to tell him—as she had fully intended—that she was going home alone, even if that meant walking back to her lodgings.

'Drew's so very protective, isn't he?' Helen mused when he had disappeared. 'I suppose it stems from his childhood—I'd begun to despair of him ever getting married. He'd seen enough of the trauma inflicted on children by the desertion of their parents ever to risk the same thing happening to his own, he once told me. Again I expect that's a legacy of the past. He doesn't talk about it much, of course, but you know how these things become public knowledge in our world, and a man in his position is so open to gossip and adverse comment. It's hard to imagine him as a vulnerable, lonely child, isn't it?'

Vulnerable? Lonely? Drew Chalmers? It certainly was! And Kirsty was curious to know what Helen meant about his childhood, but she was hardly in a position to ask. Helen plainly thought she knew all there was to know about Drew, and as his fiancée Kirsty could see that she might.

Only she wasn't Drew's fiancée, and she had no idea why he had described her as such, apart from the unpalatable suspicions she had already had.

'Here he is,' Helen exclaimed, forcing Kirsty to glance unwillingly at the familiar Porsche.

'I envy you two in a way,' were Helen's last words, as she slipped her arm through her husband's and Drew opened the passenger door of the car for Kirsty, 'being at the beginning of it all. Engagements are such a very special time, although some people seem to think they're outdated nowadays. A pity, I think.'

Thanking her for the party, Kirsty forced herself to smile an agreement she was far from feeling, as Drew put the car in gear and they moved swiftly down the drive.

'Where are we going?' she demanded angrily when he turned right instead of left at the end of the drive. 'I don't live this way.'

'I know,' came the calm retort, 'but I do, and we have things to talk about, you and I, wouldn't you say?'

'If we have whose fault is that?' Kirsty complained. 'I'm not the one who announced our engagement!'

'Calm down. I've said we'll talk about it and so we will. Right now I need all my attention on my driving. There's nothing to be afraid of, Kirsty,' he told her softly. 'I don't go in for rape, if that's what's in your mind. Unless of course it's not me you're frightened of but yourself,' he added shrewdly.

Oh, how dared he! Kirsty fumed inwardly. What did she think she was going to do? Fling herself bodily into his arms, begging for his kisses? Never, never in a million years!

Unwittingly her fingers touched her lips,

shocked by the realisation that she could still feel the firm impression of Drew's mouth against them. She had been kissed before, for goodness' sake! But never with such devastating effect, she acknowledged inwardly.

Drew negotiated the Porsche through the main street in silence, Kirsty's glance drawn, against her will, to the lean sureness of his hands as they guided the powerful car. She risked an upwards look at his face, unreadable in the half light, his mouth compressed in what could have been either obstinacy or determination. The thought struck her as it had done before that he was a man to be treated with extreme caution. He should wear a label, she decided resentfully: 'This man is dangerous.' But then he did, she acknowledged; it was there in his eyes, in the way he moved and spoke. Lost in her thoughts, she didn't realise they had taken the main road out of town, until the darkness of the landscape suddenly struck her and she turned to him.

'Don't worry,' he mocked, obviously reading her mind. 'I'm not abducting you.' He negotiated a sharp bend and turned off down a narrow lane running between high grassy banks, the drystone walling on top of them picked out by the Porsche's powerful headlight as it dipped and twisted, following the tortuous route of the road.

Eventually Drew slowed down and turned into a rutted farm track, so bumpy that even the Porsche's expensive suspension couldn't prevent Kirsty from bumping into him as the car bounced down the track. She recoiled from the intimate contact with his body immediately. His flesh was as hard and unyielding as his mind, she decided, but hard upon the heels of that thought came the vivid memory of how it had felt against her, and how her own softer body had instinctively accommodated all that male hardness, abandoning itself to it with a sensuality that still had the power to shock her.

'Are you planning to sit here all night?'

The taunting words sliced through her disturbing thoughts. She hadn't even realised they had stopped. She reached hesitantly for the door handle, stiffening as Drew reached across her, pushing aside her fumbling fingers, the musky male scent of his skin, mingled with the sharp cleanness of his cologne, reminding her intensely of that other time she had been this close to him. The intensity and complexity of the emotions such memories aroused disturbed her. She was trembling when eventually she managed to stumble from the car. They were parked in a cobbled yard, enclosed on two sides by the dark outline of a building. Behind her Kirsty heard Drew move and then light flooded the yard, and she could see that what had once been a traditional farmyard had been transformed into an attractive cobbled courtyard. Stone urns, now empty, hinted at massed flowers trailing from them during the summer, a richly russet Virginia creeper covered the walls of the farmhouse, illuminated by the lights Drew had switched on.

'Come on.'

He gripped her elbow, the rough brush of his jacket against the bare flesh of her arms acutely sensitising nerves already jangling with tension, and she jerked away, receiving a long, enigmatic look.

'I don't bite,' Drew goaded softly, 'so you can stop looking at me with those big, scared eyes.' He turned as he extracted a key and started to unlock the old-fashioned white-painted door so that she could precede him into the hall.

Kirsty guessed that a good deal of money had been spent on the farmhouse to achieve the mellowed elegance it now possessed. The hall was small and square, with an attractively beamed ceiling and plain matt walls. Several doors and a narrow set of stairs led off it, but Drew ignored these, instead opening an oak door and beckoning to her to follow him.

She did so hesitantly, watching the room come to life as Drew switched on two table lamps. The room was larger than she expected, with windows at either end, furnished traditionally with what she suspected were several very good antiques. Two large settees covered in a bold-patterned fabric dominated the room, and although it lacked the Georgian elegance of the Baileys' home, Kirsty had an immediate sense of homecoming and relaxation. Children could play happily in this room, adults could unwind in it once they had gone to bed, sharing one of those settees, perhaps, while they talked; the table lamps casting an intimate glow over them, their children sleeping upstairs. Two boys, perhaps, with dark ruffled hair and serious grey eyes.

'Something wrong?' Drew asked softly.

He was watching her closely, and her face flamed. She had always been a bit of a daydreamer, but never before had her daydreams taken on such an intimacy. How strange that when she had imagined a couple in this room, they had been Drew and herself; their children sleeping upstairs. . . . What on earth was happening to her? she asked herself crossly. The last thing she wanted was to get involved with Drew Chalmers. She disliked the man intensely. She only had to get within ten feet of him and her whole body started to react in the most unpredictable way.

'Would you like a drink? Oh, don't worry,' Drew was quick to assure her. 'I'm not proposing to get you drunk. You'd been drinking that night in Winton, hadn't you?' he asked quietly.

The suddenness of the question caught Kirsty off guard. Drinking! He made it sound so horrible and deliberate somehow, and she felt impelled to defend herself.

'One cocktail and half a bottle of wine,' she admitted, with more pain in her voice than she realised. 'I don't normally drink much at all, but I was on my own, and feeling miserable. . . .' She broke off, her face flaming, wondering what on earth had made her tell him that, but her chagrin was forgotten when he came towards her, a furious dark anger in his eyes as they moved relentlessly over her body, probing its soft contours with a knowledge that seared.

'Dear God!' It was almost a prayer, but there was no repentance in the angry line of his mouth, or the eyes that stripped her savagely of all her defences. 'What are your family thinking of? Have they never warned you of the folly of drinking too much when you can't take it? God, I thought that was the first rule parents impressed on their teenage daughters! How the hell have you managed to live so long and stay so naïve?' He shook his head, exasperation darkening his eyes as he saw her paling with the shock of his words.

'You must have been to teenage parties, surely; seen what happens when a girl has too much to drink?'

'Of course I have,' Kirsty agreed painfully. She had always avoided drinking at parties, mindful of her mother's warning that it was easy to lose control of one's ability to reason after a few drinks, and besides, having seen what happened to the girls who didn't heed their parents' advice she had made a vow that when she did make love with someone, it would be because she wanted to, and had made the decision stone cold sober.

'And yet still you went to my suite after God knows how potent a cocktail and several glasses of wine? What was it,' he jeered, 'Dutch courage? Well, we both know the result, don't we?'

'I never thought. . . .'

'That I'd be so turned on by the sight of you that I'd want you?' Drew finished brutally for her.

'You were angry with me,' Kirsty reminded him. 'You wanted to punish me.'

'And ended up punishing myself,' Drew agreed sardonically. 'But it doesn't end there, does it? Didn't you stop even once to consider some of the consequences of what you were doing?' His jacket was discarded with swift irritation, the light from the lamp behind him outlining the shape of his torso in the thin white shirt. Kirsty's mouth went dry, and a curious tension enveloped her. She closed her eyes, trying to blot out the sight of that powerful male body, the dark shadowing of body hair erotically obvious beneath the silk shirt. When had she become aware of such things? she wondered, licking dry lips; when had she first discovered that a man's body could be a beautiful thing, exciting to look at and touch? She knew the answer, but she didn't want to admit it.

'I just wanted to show you that I could act convincingly,' she got out huskily. 'I never thought I would see you again.'

'No,' Drew agreed harshly, 'you behaved like a spoiled child, and thought you could simply walk away from what you'd done and put it all behind you. Well I'm afraid life in the adult world doesn't work out quite like that, as you've discovered tonight.'

'I didn't ask you to get me a job,' Kirsty protested, stung by the validity of his criticism. 'I didn't ask you to say you were engaged to me.'

'No, you didn't,' Drew agreed heavily, 'and I've already explained my reasons for both those actions. God, you're such a child, you aren't fit to be allowed out on your own!' he announced with a savagery that sent her stomach muscles into a protesting spasm. 'That night at the hotel I could have raped you, and there wasn't a thing you could have done about it. Didn't you stop once to think about that? Is your innocence of so little value to you, that you'd carelessly throw it away, simply out of childish spite? Or are you so anxious to join the grown-up world that you're getting desperate for someone to open the door for you?' he taunted softly.

'That's a vile thing to suggest!'

'Isn't it just?' he agreed suavely. 'But one that could explain one hell of a lot.' There was an air of tension about him that puzzled Kirsty—a sort of suppressed violence that electrified the air between them and made her pulses race in reaction.

'I know you didn't announce our engagement just to save my good name!' Kirsty hurled at him childishly, driven by some deep-seated instinct to destroy the sensations threatening to engulf her. 'You can't deny that there was another reason?'

He seemed to stiffen, thick black lashes masking his expression from her.

'No,' he agreed expressionlessly. 'However, I didn't realise I'd been quite so obvious.' There was a curious pause, as though he was searching for the right words, a hesitation about him that made him seem oddly vulnerable, and for some reason the mere fact that he should be vulnerable—and show it—over Beverley Travers increased her bitterness and resentment tenfold.

'You needn't think I'm going to help you,' she told him aggressively, 'far from it. I think what you're trying to do is despicable!'

'Do you now?'

It was several seconds before Kirsty realised that the strangely flat words masked an anger far greater than any Drew had ever exhibited before, and when she did, fear trembled through her, making her rush on into incautious speech.

'Yes, I do—and to try and use a trumped-up engagement as a lever is even worse!'

'You'd have preferred me to make a laughing stock of myself and a tramp out of you by letting Beverley's comment stand—is that it? You're very naïve, Kirsty, if you honestly believe that doing so wouldn't have had repercussions—for both of us. How long do you suppose it would be before your reputation as an actress is tainted by rumours and whispers that you don't confine your ambition to appearances on stage! And me—how much longer do you suppose I would be taken seriously as a critic if it became common knowledge that I shared my bed with every little aspiring actress who climbed into it?' There was no mercy in his eyes for her pale face and stunned expression. 'Think about it,' he told her hardily, 'and you'll soon realise I'm not motivated by any quixotic impulse—our careers could be on the line here—both of them, and it's a risk I'm not prepared to take even if you are. You do realise that if you hadn't pulled that idiotic stunt in the first place none of this would have happened, and if it weren't for the fact that. . . . Oh, what the hell!' he exploded suddenly, pushing irritated fingers into his hair. 'We could argue about this all night and get nowhere. Our engagement stands, Kirsty. Any attempts by you to break it off, or to reveal the truth, and I'll make you wish you'd never been born—and if you're thinking I couldn't, think again. I grew up in a pretty hard school, and I could make you very sorry you crossed me.'

An inner voice warned her that it would be folly to press him any harder, but warring with it was a furious determination not to give in to what was tantamount to bullying.

'How?' she was tempted to demand, but the word trembled unspoken on her lips. However, Drew was obviously well aware of the train of her thoughts, because anger glittered and smouldered in his eyes as they searched her flushed and mutely defiant features.

'Oh, there are any number of ways,' he drawled coolly, 'in answer to that question so obviously burning on your tongue. At the moment the most pleasurable, as far as I'm concerned, would be to take you to my bed here and now, and teach you a lesson I'd make sure you were a long time forgetting!'

His cynicism stunned her. With one breath he was more or less admitting that he loved Beverley and would do anything to get her back, and yet with another he was coldbloodedly talking about making love to her! No, not 'making love', Kirsty amended, shuddering, but punishing, and her tender flesh quivered at the thought of Drew's hard male lips tormenting her vulnerable body, imposing on her a surrender that would stay with her for the rest of her life.

'You couldn't! The fateful words were spoken with a depth of confidence she was far from feeling, but pride insisted that she say them. To resist would be a tacit admission of defeat, an acceptance of his contention that he could bend her to his will.

He moved with a speed that frightened her into

ignominiously turning on her heel to flee. It was a repeat of those moments in his suite all over again, and if she had had the slightest atom of sense she would have hesitated before throwing down that challenge, but it had always been her way to act first and then worry about the consequences later. That was the whole trouble, she thought feverishly as Drew's fingers tightened into the soft flesh of her upper arm.

'You can't do this,' she moaned softly, not even trying to hide her fear. For a moment she thought he meant to ignore her, but then his hands fell away, his expression uncompromisingly harsh as he walked her back to the settee and pushed her down into it, taking a seat adjacent to her, but leaving a comfortable distance between them.

'Perhaps now you'll realise it isn't always wise to challenge a man to prove he's exactly that,' he told her bluntly, 'but despite that over-excited imagination of yours, Kirsty, the reason I brought you here was simply to talk through wh‚t happened tonight. Our engagement stands. I hadn't realised you knew how I felt.' His mouth compressed. 'I must admit it makes things harder—for both of us, especially since I've promised to take over directing *Much Ado* from Simon—he wants to be able to spend a little more time with Helen and Nicky. He also wants to take them on holiday this year, so you and I are going to have to work together—another reason for announcing our engagement, if you really need another. With that fertile imagination of yours, you shouldn't have much trouble accepting that if

I hadn't, *Much Ado* would have come a poor second to the attention and speculation given to our relationship—and after what Beverley said it's no use insisting that there isn't one—you wouldn't convince a single soul.'

'But you had no need to compound matters by saying we were engaged,' Kirsty flung at him. 'It's so outdated!' she shrugged petulantly. 'People don't bother with such formalities these days.'

The flash of anger in his eyes surprised her into silence.

'Meaning exactly what?' he asked coldly, 'that you'd have preferred me to announce that we were live-in lovers? It wouldn't work, Kirsty, and it would have meant you coming to live here with me, to be convincing. At least the conventionality of an engagement offers us both some measure of protection. Besides,' he added curtly, 'as a disciple of modern morals you don't put forward a very convincing case—you're still a virgin,' he reminded her, 'and something tells me that when you fall in love you're going to want permanency and commitment from your lover. What's the matter?' he goaded her when she fell silent. 'Lost for words for once?'

It wasn't that, it was simply that she was acknowledging that he was right; she would want both those things, and love as well, but what had astounded her was that Drew had known. And what was that he had said about taking over from Simon? She stared at him, her heart thudding uncomfortably.

'You're not really taking over from Simon, are

you?' she asked him huskily. 'Because if you are. . . .'

'You'll break your contract? No dice, Kirsty. Surely you haven't forgotten the effect leaving here now would have on your career, even if it was possible—which it isn't. Two flops behind you,' he reminded her cruelly, 'and then you turn down Hero? No company worth bothering with would look at you.'

Kirsty knew it was all too painfully true.

'If you really want to make it as an actress you'll put aside personal dislikes and pride, and concentrate simply on getting the most you can from the role. I still believe you can bring an important freshness to Hero, and Simon agrees with me.'

'I don't know if I can work with you,' Kirsty told him honestly, appalled by the sudden explosion of anger in his eyes.

'Do you think it will be easy for me?' he blazed at her. 'God, what a child you are! And let's not pretend that I couldn't undermine those defences of yours very easily, Kirsty—very easily indeed. And don't start telling me again that I'd have to force you. It wouldn't take much. This, for instance. . . .'

He moved before she could stop him, crossing the space that divided them, his body pressing her back against the soft cushions, his tongue trailing enticingly along the vulnerable curve of her throat. Weakness invaded her, the terrible shattering knowledge that he was right, and that her body responded passionately to him, no matter how much she willed it not to, something she could no longer deny.

'You see?' Drew mocked softly. His hands cupped her shoulders, warm fingers probing the narrow straps of her dress as he bent his head again, intent on further destruction of her willpower. Kirsty quivered tensely beneath the expert assault of his mouth, moving lazily over skin that seemed to possess a thousand receptive nerve endings, each one relaying to her brain the delirious pleasure his touch invoked. His teeth caught her earlobe, teasing it gently. It was like drowning, Kirsty thought numbly; like going down for the third time and not caring about anything except the sensually fatal embrace of a danger that whispered seductively of pleasure to come, blotting out reason and logic. Her shoulders were now bared to the seeking warth of his touch, but she no longer cared. The tormenting movement of his lips against her skin driving her to a shivering insanity that demanded the hard pressure of his mouth against hers, plunging her into the hot, sweet vortex of desire he had shown her before, his touch a siren song that deafened her to everything else.

As though he read her wayward thoughts, Drew explored the shape of her lips, teasing them with the tip of his tongue, until her mouth parted like the petals of a flower, embracing the bee that sought its sweetness.

Drew's hands moved downwards, taking her dress with them, but Kirsty no longer cared as the hard, lean fingers covered the lacy cups of her bra, their heat burning through the thin fabric to her skin as Drew moved in restless urgency against her, his mouth bruising hers and drawing from her a response that shocked and scorched her, but which was too powerful for her to resist the compulsive urge to let her fingers slide between the pearl buttons of his shirt to stroke feverishly against the warmth of his chest.

Drew groaned, moving so that both of them were lying on the settee, wrenching open the buttons on his shirt with swift impatience and lifting his mouth from Kirsty's long enough to demand thickly that she touch him.

She needed no second bidding. There was a dark heady pleasure in simply allowing her hands to move over the heated male flesh, exploring the texture and feel of it.

'Kirsty!'

She trembled as Drew released her lips, his mouth seeking out the swelling curves of her breasts, highlighted by the lamp's glow, which lent her skin a soft honey sheen, the taut thrust of her breasts heightened by the lacy structure of her bra. A thrill of wanton desire flooded through her as Kirsty glanced down and saw the darkness of Drew's hair against her flesh. Her breasts throbbed with an aching tension that half frightened her. Drew's voice thickened unsteadily as he muttered something against her skin, reaching for the fastening, and Kirsty felt her breath stifle in her throat as he freed her aroused nipples from the constraining lace.

All at once her body seemed alien to her. No man had ever evoked this reaction from her before, and she moaned softly with a need deeply desired, but unknown, until Drew's thumbs rubbed gently over the swollen peaks, his mouth moving slowly over her creamy skin until it finally possessed the aching fullness.

The whole world seemed to explode in a dizzying mass of sensation, as Kirsty arched instinctively beneath him, hands clinging to the breadth of his shoulders as she sobbed his name and pressed tiny half demented kisses against the musky dampness of his skin.

Excitement and anticipation spiralled up inside her, and it came as a shock to realise that Drew was releasing her, that his heartbeat which had pounded erratically against her was slowing and steadying while hers still raced.

At last when she could bear the silence with which he searched his face no longer, she burst out in a voice that shook with mingled shame and despair.

'I suppose you think that proves something, but any experienced man could have had the same effect. Any experienced man.'

He was quiet for so long her nerves coiled into hard knots of tension.

'If that's true,' he said at last, sitting up and reaching for his shirt, 'then I feel very sorry for you.'

It stunned and completely deflated her. She had expected furious disbelief; argument, anything but that quiet contempt. For a moment she was almost tempted to withdraw the words; to admit that. . . . That what? she asked herself in dawning shock. That he was the *only* man who could make her feel like that? But that would mean . . . that would mean. . . . She struggled heroically and then at the last minute lost her courage and told herself that all it meant was that she was extraordinarily susceptible to him, that was all. The other—that awful and tenuous suspicion that she might actually have fallen in love with him, was not to be borne, so she dismissed it, clinging hard to reason and logic, both of which assured her that it was completely impossible to fall in love with a man one disliked as much as she disliked Drew.

'What are you waiting for?' The cruel voice goaded her into awareness. 'Me to dress you?'

Kirsty's face coloured, her fingers clumsy as she reached for her clothes. He made no attempt to look away as she struggled, and to her consternation Kirsty felt her breasts flower into awareness of his gaze, the nipples firm and hard, her breasts swelling slightly.

'Allow me.' Drew's touch was completely impersonal. It was all different for men, Kirsty thought, choking back weak tears. They could easily make love to one woman while really loving another. Physical desire for them had nothing to do with any nobler emotion. What would Drew do if she threatened to tell Beverley Travers about this? Nothing, probably, she admitted. In fact he would probably feel that it would only advance his cause and increase Beverley Travers' jealousy. For the other woman had been jealous, Kirsty acknowledged that, and no doubt Drew hoped that by flaunting his mock engagement to her, he would get her back.

Why on earth should that thought cause her so much pain? Once he had succeeded she would be free to leave; she would never have to see him again, which was surely what she wanted.

'I'll drive you home,' Drew announced abruptly, adding huskily, 'I take it what happened just now hasn't changed your mind?'

Kirsty went red and white with the cruelty of it. He must be completely insensitive if he could make love to her with one breath and ask her to help him get Beverley back in the next. And yet she had thought him a man of acute perception. Perhaps it was true that love blinded people to the feelings of others.

'Nothing you could either say or do could make me do that,' she threw at him through gritted teeth. 'Nothing!'

For a moment his face seemed to be carved out of granite, masklike and taut, and she had the strangest feeling that it was concealing almost unbearable pain, containing it only with the greatest effort of will, but the moment was gone before she could question it. Drew was on his feet, pulling on his coat and handing her hers, opening the door so that she could precede him through it, and she told herself the regret and loneliness she felt as he closed it after them, shutting out its warmth and intimacy, was merely an illusion and had nothing to be with the fact that the closing of the door was symbolic of the fact that he was shutting her out of his life.

CHAPTER FIVE

A PRE-REHEARSAL meeting had been called by Drew for Sunday afternoon, and Kirsty had been up early, too nervous to settle down and read through the play again as she had planned. Instead she rang her parents, answering her mother's anxious queries absently, wondering what Mrs Stannard would say if she were to tell her the truth. How could she have let Drew force her into a fictitious engagement? At the very first opportunity she fully intended to break it. But how? An idea took shape in her mind, causing her to abandon her chair by the window and the thumbed copy of *Much Ado* she had been studying.

Drew was a fiercely proud man; his attitude towards Beverley Travers had proved that. He had forced Kirsty into their 'engagement' solely to punish the other girl, she was sure of this, but what if she, Kirsty, turned the tables on him and made it impossible for him to continue their 'engagement' and still retain his pride? But how? One simple solution presented itself to her, and although she quailed a little from it, the memory of the emotions she had experienced in Drew's arms, compared with his very evident lack of them, compelled her. What she had in mind was a flirtation with someone else, and to make it obvious enough to force Drew into bringing their 'engagement' to an end. But would it work? She didn't know, but felt that it was a chance she must take; anything to free herself from playing the false and unacceptable role of Drew's loving fiancée.

Firmly ignoring the small inner voice that whispered that she found the role all the more onerous for being false, she concentrated on laying her plans.

Cherry had already pointed Clive out to her as being the company's recognised flirt. Kirsty had seen the way he had looked at her, and recognised in him a certain devil-may-care attitude which would probably incline him towards a flirtation with a girl supposedly attached to another man; especially a man such as Drew, she thought intuitively. Clive was slightly jealous of Drew. She had seen it in his eyes, and had noticed the slight pique with which he had heard the announcement of their engagement.

And there would be no need to be particularly subtle. Clive wouldn't need much encouragement, and she could not see Drew accepting his supposed fiancée's flirtation with another man with any great degree of complacency whether that fiancée was real or not. The best thing, she mused, would be if she could provoke Drew into a public quarrel, one where she could trap him into giving her the sort of ultimatum she could react to with tears and a very definite breaking off of their supposed relationship.

It gave her a few uncomfortable moments to know that her plans would shock and distress her parents, but Drew scarcely merited any tender consideration of his finer feelings after the way he had treated her. He was using her, and would have no grounds for objection if she turned the tables on him! She would do anything to be free of the odium of their engagement—anything! She couldn't endure another scene like the one she had undergone last night. Her skin still felt scorched by his touch, her body almost frighteningly alien to her. It had alarmed her how easily he had aroused her, and how callously. It must be his greater experience—she refused to allow herself to even contemplate any other explanation for her response.

Rather than drive down to the theatre, she decided to walk. It was a cold, crisp afternoon, with the leaves crunchy underfoot, and walking along the river bank was a pleasure rather than a hardship. She had dressed casually for the rehearsal—jeans, a baggy jumper over her thin tee-shirt and a pair of suede boots she had bought the previous winter and which were now beginning to look rather scuffed.

And yet several of the people she passed, walking in the opposite direction, turned to glance admiringly at her slender figure in the faded jeans and maroon sweater, her dark hair curling wildly round a face more piquant than beautiful, her skin healthily flushed and a vivaciousness about the way she moved that made them envy her her lack of years.

Kirsty was oblivious to their regard, intent only on getting to the theatre and putting her plan into action. Inactivity didn't suit her, and her eyes glowed with resolution, determination firming her chin.

So Mr Drew Chalmers thought he could push her around and force her to fall in with his schemes, did he? Well, it was high time he realised that he was wrong. Very wrong!

Most of the others were already gathered in the theatre when Kirsty arrived. Cherry was busy making coffee, and produced a mug for her, warning her that everyone was expected to provide their own. 'You'll be able to pick one up at the weekly market,' she told Kirsty. 'Unless, of course, you intend to share your beloved's.'

Kirsty swallowed the bitter retort hovering on the tip of her unruly tongue and produced a rather forced smile. Cherry meant well, and after all, she didn't realise the true situation.

'Kirsty, you're five minutes late!'

Nothing could have been less lover-like than the snapped sentence.

One or two of the others looked surprised as well, and Kirsty bent her head over her steaming mug, not wanting Drew to see the flash of rebellious resentment in her eyes. Of course, he had a position to maintain. He was going to direct them and no doubt would not want the others suggesting that she was favoured because of their supposed personal relationship.

'Whew, what's got into him?' Cherry whispered as she came to collect the mugs. Drew was talking to the actress who was to play Beatrice, and Kirsty shrugged carelessly, indicating that she neither knew nor cared.

'Not had a lovers' quarrel, have we?' murmured Clive dulcetly, coming over to join them. 'Ah, Kirsty my love, if I were engaged to you, I'd be so busy making love to you there wouldn't be time to quarrel!'

Here was her chance! Kirsty took a deep breath and smiled at him provocatively. 'Drew's a very busy man,' she told him, giving a small, pained sigh. 'I'd no idea when I came up here that I'd see so little of him. It isn't a bit like I'd imagined.'

She was aware that Cherry, at her side, was looking rather surprised, but Clive's smile was edged with satisfaction, the pressure of his fingers, gently squeezing her arm, slightly more than merely comforting.

'Been neglecting you, has he?' he murmured softly. 'Poor little girl! We'll have to see if we can't find some way of entertaining you when he's too busy.'

'Kirsty—Clive, if I could have your attention for a moment!'

Kirsty had been so engrossed in fostering Clive's impression that Drew was neglecting her and she was peeved about it, that she hadn't realised that the rest of the cast had gathered round Drew.

Consequently there was no need for her to fake embarrassment or the guilty look she exchanged with Clive, and Drew's brows came together in a frown as she hurried over.

'I've just been explaining to the others what we want to achieve from *Much Ado*. We haven't done it before as a company, and both Simon and I feel it needs a fresh approach. As I think most of you already know, Simon is handing over to me for *Much Ado*. He wants to spend some time with Helen, and he also wants to go to New York, to see the sort of thing they're doing over there. We're hoping that next season we might be able to extend our repertoire slightly . . .'

'But you don't normally direct, surely?'

It was David Andrews, who was to play Benedick, who asked the question. A popular actor, he was also extremely dedicated to turning out a professional performance, and Kirsty could see faint concern shadowing his eyes as he asked the question.

'Not normally,' Drew agreed with a smile that said he understood the reasoning behind the question and respected him for it. 'Certainly I did at Oxford, and for several years afterwards, but these days, when I'm not writing, I work mainly as a critic.'

Writing! Kirsty hadn't realised that he wrote, and she wondered how many more strings he had to his bow.

'However,' Drew was continuing, 'if at any time the cast feels that I'm letting them down, they're perfectly at liberty to say so.'

'It's a pitty we aren't doing one of your plays,' David Andrews further astounded Kirsty by saying. 'I saw *Light Waves* being performed at the National during the summer. Peter Howard made an excellent Leo.'

Light Waves! Kirsty was stunned. *Light Waves* had been written by Paul Bennett, a much revered and admired modern playwright they had studied at drama school, one of the few modern playwrights Kirsty admired. It came as a shocking blow to realise that Paul

Bennett and Drew Chalmers were one and the same person.

Across the small distance that separated them she could see the open mockery in Drew's eyes and held herself proudly. Was it her fault that she hadn't known?

'Quite a man, your fiancé,' Clive murmured softly at her side. 'That's where he got the money to invest in the place. But of course, you'll already know all about that, won't you?'

Kirsty wasn't too naïve to sense the hostility and envy behind the question, but before she could say anything Rachel Bellamy, who was playing Beatrice, was speaking, her voice rather cool as she said sharply, 'Drew, I've heard that you're planning to change Hero's role slightly. I can understand why, of course,' her eyes rested with icy disdain on Kirsty's flushed cheeks, 'but I must say, darling, it isn't like you to allow emotion to run away with common sense. Hero is merely a foil to Beatrice . . .'

'And so the audience feels a great deal of sympathy for her,' Drew pointed out. 'As far as the relationship between Beatrice and Hero is concerned, I don't want to change it, but when it comes to Hero's acceptance of Claudio's denunciation of her and their subsequent reunion, I should like to see her behaving in a way that today's woman can more easily identify with.'

'But surely even today, there are women who accept just as much from their men as Hero did?' Kirsty surprised herself by saying.

It was disconcerting to have so many pairs of eyes fixed on her face, not all of them kind.

It was Rachel who spoke first.

'Oh dear,' she exclaimed in dulcet tones, 'are we about to witness a lovers' quarrel? Haven't you told her yet, Drew, that one simply does not argue with the director, even when one is engaged to him?'

To Kirsty's surprise Drew, instead of looking annoyed, merely said calmly, 'Kirsty wasn't arguing with me, Rachel, and she does have a valid point. However, in this instance both Simon and I believe that Hero has been thrust too much into the background in past productions. Now, I want to run through the entire play. Everyone knows what part they're taking. We'll read through and then talk about it afterwards.'

The casual way he said it gave Kirsty no intimation whatsoever of how hard they were all going to have to work. The simple read-through took the best part of five hours, with Drew constantly stopping them and explaining exactly what he wanted from each actor.

It was nearly seven in the evening when he finally glanced at his watch and announced, 'I think we'd better break there. Don't forget, we start rehearsals proper on Tuesday morning.'

Kirsty had been sitting next to Rafe Adams who was playing Claudio. She liked him and thought they would work well together, although the read-through had brought home to her more than ever just how hard she was going to have to work. Clive joined them as they stood up.

'How about giving me a lift back into town?' he suggested to Kirsty, obviously not realising that she hadn't come in her car. 'Then we could go out and have a Chinese if you fancy the idea. I expect your ever-loving will have to stay behind to smooth down la Bellamy——' he gestured in the direction of Rachel Bellamy. 'She wasn't too happy about the idea of him boosting your part— I can see why, of course. She's frightened you'll upstage her—probably with good reason,' he added flatteringly. 'So I'm afraid your fiancé will be lost to you for tonight. One of the penalties of mingling with the famous!'

Kirsty really had no desire to do anything other than return to her bedsit and simply flop. Reluctant though she was to admit it even to herself, pique had mingled with the relief she had experienced when she realised that far from subjecting her to any lover-like displays of affection, Drew was behaving towards her exactly as he behaved towards the rest of the cast.

She was just on the point of explaining to Clive that she hadn't come in her car, when Drew's voice suddenly silenced her.

'Kirsty!' he called.

She turned her head, and Clive murmured mischievously in her ear, 'Ah. His Master's Voice, and how well he has you trained, my dear . . . I hear that Beverley Travers is staying with Rachel and her husband, for an unspecified length of time,' he added. 'I should be very careful if I were you. She won't give him up lightly.'

'Have you got a moment?' Drew asked. 'There are one or two points I should like to go over with you . . .'

'Oh, unfair, darling!' Rachel pouted resentfully.

'Surely you can give Kirsty extra coaching any time? I wanted you to come back and have dinner with us. There are one or two aspects of Beatrice I want to talk over with you. I'm sure Kirsty won't mind, will you, sweet?'

Inwardly seething, Kirsty forced a vapid smile. Rachel didn't fool her in the least, and she would have laid bets that Drew would find himself partnered for dinner by Beverley Travers.

Still, was that any concern of hers? she chided herself. Drew had made no secret of his feelings for the other woman. She herself was merely a pawn in the game.

'Of course I don't,' she managed with a sweetness to match Rachel's. 'Drew has already explained to me that being director often means that business has to come before pleasure. Never mind, darling,' she smiled up at him, watching the way Rachel's eyes hardened with anger as she slipped her hand through Drew's arm and gazed up at him, 'we can always make up for it later.'

'There you are, Drew!' Rachel exclaimed triumphantly. 'I knew Kirsty would understand. I'd invite her to join us, but I'm sure she'd much rather be with the other young things, at the pub. I can remember how much we used to enjoy that sort of thing, can't you?'

She was clever, Kirsty conceded, watching her smile. If Drew had really been engaged to her, by now both of them would be feeling a little sore; she would be imagining that she was too young for Drew, and no doubt he would be wondering if he was too old for her. However, Kirsty realised soon that she had underestimated him, for instead of appearing put out by Rachel's malice, he merely thanked her for the invitation, and told Kirsty he would talk to her later about Hero, dropping a brief kiss on her forehead before leaving with Rachel.

Kirsty saw them briefly when she and the others emerged from the theatre. Drew was climbing into the back seat of Alan's powerful Daimler.

'Don't look so forlorn,' Cherry told her commiseratingly. 'I don't think there's any doubt as to who he'd rather be with.'

Kirsty didn't either, but she knew that Cherry would be both shocked and disbelieving if she were to tell her what she thought, so instead she forced a smile and announced that she rather regretted not bringing the car, because the evening was sharply cold after the warmth of the theatre, and she was not really in the mood for the walk home.

'A word of warning before you go,' Cherry cautioned her. 'Clive—I know he's a charmer, but I got the impression that Drew wasn't too happy about the way the pair of you were chatting away together.'

Kirsty endeavoured to look both disbelieving and faintly sullen. 'Drew doesn't choose my friends for me,' she told Cherry.

Cherry looked unconvinced and rather concerned, and Kirsty hated herself for deceiving the older girl. However, there was no way she could tell her the truth.

'Don't worry,' she palliated, 'Drew isn't the possessive type.'

Cherry gave her a distinctly old-fashioned look. 'No?' she questioned with irony. 'My dear, if you believe that you'll believe anything! Drew was looking at you with a distinctly proprietorial look in his eyes. All men in love are jealous to some extent, love,' she added, 'and your Drew's no different. If anything I should think he's worse than average. Those cool, deceptive ones always are.'

When Clive realised that Kirsty wasn't in her car, he begged a lift from one of the others, leaving Kirsty to walk home on her own. In many ways she wasn't sorry. The read-through had been exhilarating in many ways, and she had left the theatre with her mind crammed with new impressions and ideas, and yet it was Drew who occupied her thoughts to the exclusion of everything else as she walked homewards—Drew, who would probably by now be sitting in Rachel Bellamy's drawing room, sipping sherry and exchanging polite conversation with the love of his life, while Rachel looked on approvingly.

Of course, it was natural that she should champion her friend, Kirsty admitted, and yet somehow she couldn't help feeling sorry for Drew, condemned to spend the rest of his life with a woman as cold and hard as Beverley Travers.

As the direction of her wayward thoughts suddenly struck her she came to an abrupt standstill. What on earth was happening to her? If she should feel sorry for anyone, it ought to be herself!

Her small bedsit looked remarkably cosy and

attractive with the curtains drawn and the one solitary lamp giving a soft glow to the faded chintz settee and pale beige carpet, Kirsty decided as she glanced proudly round the room. On the cane dresser were several photographs of her family, and she had bought some flowers on Saturday which added a bright splash of colour and homeliness to the room. Her mother was a natural homemaker and Kirsty had inherited much of her flair. She decided to wash her hair before she ate, and changed into a pretty candy-striped cotton nightshirt she had bought during the summer, before going into the small bathroom. The nightshirt was pretty enough to wear over jeans had she wished to do so, and more comfortable for relaxing in.

She had just wrapped her wet hair in a towel and wandered into the kitchen to whisk eggs for the omelette she had decided to make when she heard her doorbell ring.

Expecting it to be Cherry, she opened the door with a warm smile, which faded when she saw Drew standing there, tall and leanly powerful in the dark trousers and leather jacket she had seen him leaving the theatre in earlier.

'That's what I like,' he drawled in irony. 'A warm welcome from my loving fiancée! Aren't you going to ask me in?'

Kirsty had stepped back automatically, and he followed her in, filling the tiny foyer.

'I thought you were having dinner, with Rachel and her husband,' she began stupidly, flushing when he drawled, 'Now what on earth gave you that impression? Or do I look like the kind of man who leaves his fiancée to starve while he dines with his ex-girl-friend?'

When he said it, Kirsty guessed why he had left early. 'Of course, you told them you were coming here,' she guessed distastefully. 'I trust Beverley was suitably jealous?'

'If she was, she hid it very well,' he told her, suddenly frowning as he took in her appearance.

'I was planning to have an early night,' Kirsty stammered, cheeks flushing in anger. She had no need to explain her actions to anyone, least of all Drew, nor to feel embarrassed by them.

'Without eating?'

'I was just going to make myself an omelette,' she told him defensively. 'It's been a tiring day— and after last night. . . .'

'Ah yes, last night.' His eyes mocked her. 'That's one of the reasons I wanted to see you. Tomorrow I'm taking you into York to get your engagement ring. I'll pick you up at eleven. We'll have lunch somewhere, talk over your part. I wanted to discuss it with you anyway.'

'And this way you can kill two birds with one stone?' Kirsty suggested tightly. God, the arrogance of the man! 'I don't want a ring,' she told him. 'It isn't necessary.'

'It is to me,' Drew told her. 'If only to stop young fools like Clive Richmond from flirting with you.'

'And spoiling all your plans?' Kirsty ventured, bitterly angry without knowing why. Why should she care if all Drew thought about was Beverley Travers, if she was the only woman who meant anything to him emotionally? They deserved one another, she told herself; and she didn't give a damn about either of them.

'Why don't you go and dry your hair,' Drew suggested, surprising her, 'and I'll make us both that omelette.'

Kirsty wanted to say that she didn't want to share her supper with him and that she would much rather eat alone, but the words even merely framed in her head sounded ungracious, and besides, there were several points she had been mulling over about her part that she did want to discuss with him.

'A first-rate director,' Helen had called him, and Kirsty suspected that she could very well be right, much as it went against the grain to say so.

She dried her hair briskly with a towel, taking the precaution of changing back into her jeans and a clean jumper, something which didn't escape Drew's sardonic eyes when she went back into the small kitchen.

'You needn't have worried,' he told her dryly, 'I didn't come here to make love to you.'

Kirsty turned away, willing herself not to colour up. Of course she hadn't thought that he had, it was just that she hadn't felt comfortable dressed merely in her shirt, while he was wearing an expensive cashmere sweater and equally costly-looking pants. The leather jacket had been discarded and lay on a chair, but Kirsty could tell simply by looking at it that it was as expensive as the rest of his outfit.

'Omelette's ready. Here, pass me the plates, will you,' Drew instructed. 'They're heating under the grill.'

They ate off trays on their knees—a strangely intimate scene, and one that caused Kirsty an inexplicable pang. What did it matter to her if Drew was merely using her? she asked herself. She fully intended to turn the tables on him. But somehow it did matter. She stole a look at him beneath her lashes as she finished off the omelette. He was so handsome, so virilely masculine that she doubted that any woman could remain impervious to him for long, but there was more to him than that. She was intelligent and articulate, and to the woman he loved would be a companion and friend as well as a lover. What was happening to her? Kirsty wondered, the omelette suddenly tasting like rubber. She loathed the man! He was overbearing and domineering; everything she detested in a man.

'I hope this sacrifice has the desired effect,' she told him acidly as she collected their empty plates. 'Just think, you could have been dining in luxury with Beverley Travers!'

'But instead I chose to eat with the woman I love,' Drew mocked. 'Although I doubt that they'd believe me—that I came here to eat, I mean,' he told her. 'I suspect they thought I had very different appetites in mind when I said my goodbyes.'

For the life of her Kirsty couldn't meet his eyes.

'It's late,' she told him in a strained voice. 'I think you ought to be going.' Somehow any reference to the way she had felt in his arms, no matter how oblique, made her stomach churn in protest.

'How very timid you are! I thought in these modern days girls no longer feared being alone with their intended husband and his unbridled passion.'

'That hardly applies in our case,' Kirsty told him stiffly. 'I'm simply tired, that's all. It's been a long day . . .'

'And looks like being an even longer night,' Drew drawled in a curiously bitter tone. It struck Kirsty then that there were faint shadows beneath his eyes, a look of strain round his mouth, and she wondered how much he felt the deprivation of being without Beverley, who had undoubtedly spent more than one night wrapped in his arms.

It was several seconds before it dawned on her that the emotions aroused by the mental picture she had conjured up were those of pain and envy, and several more for her to come to terms with them sufficiently for her to get to her feet and walk numbly towards the door.

'Kirsty . . .' Drew's hand was on her arm, a more understanding expression in his eyes than she had ever seen before. 'I know this is hard for you,' he told her, 'but I . . .' He frowned suddenly, black brows snapping together as the doorbell pealed.

'A late visitor,' he remarked. 'Were you expecting someone?'

'No.' She flushed as his eyes lingered intently on her face, suddenly feeling like a guilty schoolgirl, for no reason at all.

The bell pealed again and she moved towards it and opened the door.

'At last—I'd begun to think you'd gone to bed!' Clive stepped in through the open door, bending to nuzzle her neck and murmur appreciatively, 'Umm, you smell nice. What is it?'

'Forbidden.'

Drew's icy voice stopped him in his tracks, and his head lifted as he drawled appreciatively and without the slightest trace of embarrassment, 'Oh dear! Sorry about that, lovey, but I thought . . .'

'*I* think you should leave,' Drew interrupted suavely.

For a moment Kirsty thought Clive would debate the issue, and then he shrugged lightly, smiling as he turned back towards the door, murmuring sotto voce to Kirsty, 'Another time, perchance, oh fair one,' and then he was gone, leaving Kirsty alone to face the icy coldness of Drew's eyes, feeling as guilty as though they had in truth been engaged.

'I didn't ask him to call——' she began defensively,

'I don't expect you did,' Drew agreed. 'His type never need asking, although God knows you were giving all the encouragement he could have wanted this afternoon. I ignored it because I thought it was all pique, but perhaps I was wrong? Is he what you want from life, Kirsty?'

'He was being friendly, that's all. He felt sorry for me because I was on my own . . .'

'Is that so? Now I got a completely different impression,' Drew told her with iron inflexibility. 'I thought he knew quite well that you were engaged to me and that he wanted to do a little poaching in safe water—safe for him, that is.'

Kirsty fired up indignantly. 'You're wrong! He was just being friendly . . .'

'Very friendly,' Drew drawled in agreement. 'Friendly enough to call around at . . .' he shook back the sleeve of his sweater to glance at his watch, 'nearly eleven at night. You would have offered him a cup of coffee, of course, by which time it would have been twelve-ish—he has lodgings in York, unless I'm mistaken, with some of the other bit players, and the last bus leaves at eleven-fifteen. What would you have done, Kirsty—suggested that he walk home, or offered him a bed here? Your bed, perhaps?'

'That's a vile thing to suggest!' Kirsty protested indignantly. 'Must everyone have an ulterior motive? Couldn't he simply have been wanting to be friendly?'

'Not where you're concerned,' he told her brutally, 'and if all he had in mind was a platonic friendship, I'm no judge of character. But then of course men in love are notorious for their lack of judgment,' he added with fine irony. 'One thing's for sure—he wasn't expecting to see me here.'

'He heard Rachel Bellamy asking you to dine with them,' Kirsty told him brittlely.

'And felt sorry for my poor deserted little fiancée, all uncared for and unloved. Perhaps I'd better correct that impression—don't worry,' Drew told her, when her eyes widened, 'I have no intention of spending the night on your settee—there are other ways,' he told her enigmatically. 'Starting with getting my ring on your finger.'

When he had gone, Kirsty found it curiously difficult to get to sleep, despite her tiredness. What was the matter with her? she asked herself restlessly. The sooner she was free of this bogus engagement the better. And everything was working out so well. Clive appearing unexpectedly as he had done had plainly aroused Drew's suspicions. All she had to do was to fan them to the point when it provoked a confrontation—and yet she had a curious revulsion for what she had to do. It brought her down to the level of Beverley Travers and Drew, she thought fastidiously.

CHAPTER SIX

THE fine weather continued as Drew drove them towards York. He had picked Kirsty up just before eleven. She had been ready and waiting for him, choosing, on some impulse she couldn't quite define herself, to wear an expensive, fine tweed suit Chelsea had given her when she left college. The plums and greys were a perfect foil for her own dark colouring, and with it she wore a plain grey silk blouse she had bought in Harrods sale.

If she had expected Drew to be impressed by the care she had taken with her appearance she was disappointed. He murmured only a brief greeting and then escorted her to the waiting car, opening the door for her and seeing her safely inside before driving off.

As she glanced surreptitiously at him it came to Kirsty how little she knew about him, and yet here they were practically on the verge of getting engaged, albeit temporarily. Did he have a family, close friends who might be expected to want to know about their supposed 'engagement'? It was hard for her to imagine him in a family setting, for some reason he struck her quite forcibly as a loner, but somewhere he must have parents; perhaps other relatives . . .

'You're looking worried—what's the matter this time?'

Kirsty hadn't realised he had switched his glance from the road to her, and caught unawares by the steely perception of his eyes she blurted out unthinkingly, 'I was just wondering about your family—what they might think about . . .'

'I have no family.' His voice was clipped, his face shuttered and repressive.

'No . . . but . . .'

'Oh, I had parents once—if you could call them that. A mother who cheated on her marriage and then when she found herself pregnant by her lover deserted the child she bore, while her lover disappeared, somewhere in the Australian outback. They're both dead now,' he told Kirsty coldly, 'and if it wasn't for the compassion of my mother's husband, I doubt if I'd know even today who my parents actually were.'

The brooding quality of the words struck Kirsty to the heart. Surrounded all her life by her parents' almost doting affection, she found it hard to accept that any parents could simply abandon their child as Drew was suggesting.

'What's the matter?' he demanded sardonically. 'Don't you believe me? Or is it simply that you want to hear all the unpleasant details?'

When she made a brief sound of denial in her throat, he grimaced. 'Perhaps it's just as well this engagement isn't real, otherwise you might legitimately question who you were marrying. It's a terrible thing to deprive a child of all knowledge of its parents; it creates a vacuum that no one who hasn't experienced it can understand; a sense of being set apart from the rest of society and oneself; a loss of identity that lurks in the shadows like a childhood nightmare.'

Listening to him, Kirsty remembered what Helen had told her on the night of her party. Now her words started to make sense. Was this what she had meant about Drew being reluctant to commit himself to marriage? Was it because he himself . . .

'You have a very expressive face,' he told her roughly. 'I can almost see the word "bastard" written on it in six-inch-high letters!'

'No . . . no . . . I was just thinking how terrible it must have been for you as a child,' Kirsty told him honestly.

'Not at first. I was brought up in a children's home with "others of my kind".' His mouth was wry. 'It was only when I reached my teens that I realised fully what that meant. Those were agonising years—knowing nothing about myself except the fact that I had been abandoned as a baby. I was fifteen before I learned the truth, and then only by chance. My mother's husband had found her letters to her lover on her death and on going through them had realised she had had a child and that they had decided between them to abandon it. He started to look for me—not out of any sense of maudlin sentiment but because he truly believed she had done wrong in leaving me with no means of discovering anything of my roots. I liked him. He died two years ago, unfortunately . . .'

'And your father?' Kirsty prompted softly, a huge lump in her throat. It was silly to feel so much pain for a man she positively hated, and yet she did—oh, not pain for the man he was, but pain for the child he had been—bitter, deserted . . .

'Like I said, he went to Australia when my mother discovered she was pregnant and he died there six years afterwards. Both of them were only children, so if you're expecting to gain a family as well as a fiancé I'm afraid you're doomed to disappointment.'

'Was it very dreadful?' Kirsty asked quietly. 'I. . . .'

'Save your sympathy for those more deserving of it,' Drew told her dryly. 'I've come to terms with my birth a long time ago. I just wish to God these kids who glibly get themselves pregnant and then find out the hard way that being a single parent in Surbiton doesn't measure up to the Hollywood image of having a "love-child" would think a little more about the child they're creating and a little less about themselves.'

He was a man of strange contrasts, Kirsty reflected to herself as he turned away from her to concentrate on his driving, and plainly there were scars, however much he tried to hide them. No doubt this was why he had been wary of marriage, but now he had found Beverley and he wanted total commitment from her; the sort of commitment his mother had denied him when she deserted him for the sake of propriety, Kirsty realised with sudden insight.

'Do you . . . do you hate your mother very much?' she whispered hesitantly. 'It must have been dreadful for you.'

For a moment she thought he wasn't going to

reply. He was frowning, staring out of the window.

'I don't think I ever hated her,' he said at last. 'She was a victim, of circumstance and her own emotions, but I can't deny that I'd prefer to see a world where children don't have to grow up not knowing their parents' names. You might bear that in mind the next time you invite yourself into a man's bedroom.'

Was that why he had stopped when he did? Because he didn't want to be guilty of the same crime as his mother's lover?

'Stop looking so desperate,' he advised her wryly. 'It's something I came to terms with years ago; these things happen.'

'But not to you?' Kirsty guessed, watching him. He was dressed in casual cords and a chunky sweater today, a soft pale grey leather blouson jacket open over his sweater; emphasising the breadth of his shoulders and the muscled suppleness of his body.

'Not if I can help it,' he agreed. 'Which is why . . .'

He broke off to negotiate a dangerous bend, but Kirsty didn't need to hear the words to guess what he had been intending to say; something to the effect that that was why he was using her to make Beverley jealous. He loved the other woman, but he wanted more than an affair with her—and yet he would have to be very sure of a woman before he committed himself fully to her, Kirsty could see that now; sure that she loved him and that she would be faithful to him. He wouldn't be the first man in Beverley Travers' life; perhaps the rich divorcee had already hinted that they simply continue as lovers and this was his way of showing her that he wanted more. Perhaps he was hoping that Beverley would be jealous enough of her to commit herself completely to him.

They drove in silence the rest of the way to York, where Drew parked on the outskirts, just outside the city walls, then he took Kirsty's arm to guide her across the busy street. Once the other side had been reached Kirsty expected him to release her, but he didn't. Perhaps he was expecting to bump into someone from the cast, she thought acidly, disliking this public display of 'affection', knowing how insecure it was. She couldn't think of any other reason for the distinctly proprietorial manner in which he tucked his hand under her elbow, holding her close enough for her to feel his body heat as they manoeuvred their way through the other shoppers.

It was plain that Drew knew York well, because he wasted little time, hurrying her towards Parliament Square with its banks and finance houses and then down one of the narrow little wynds leading off it, where Kirsty could have spent hours entranced in front of the mouthwatering shop windows with their displays of craft goods and elegant clothes, but Drew ignored them all, and Kirsty was hard put to it to keep pace with his long strides.

He stopped at last outside a small, discreetly expensive jewellers. Several stunning items of jewellery adorned the small window, and Drew explained as they went inside that it was owned by a craftsman who made his own pieces.

The girl who came forward to serve them was friendly and obviously interested in her work. So why should she feel this spark of resentment at the way she looked admiringly at Drew? Kirsty asked herself.

When Drew explained what they wanted her face fell a little. She retreated to the rear of the shop and an older man emerged in her place.

'My assistant tells me you are looking for an engagement ring?' When Drew nodded, he smiled, and asked Kirsty if she had any preference.

She shook her head, a curiously heavy sensation taking possession of her chest. Somehow what they were doing made a mockery of all her childhood romantic dreams of this moment, when a man bestowed upon her what was supposed to be a pledge of his love.

'I have,' Drew announced, startling her. He murmured something to the man, who beamed and disappeared, reappearing several seconds later holding a large leather case.

When he opened it, Kirsty caught her breath in awe.

'They're all so lovely,' she expostulated, 'I . . .'

'Try this one.' Very quietly Drew handed her a barked band of gold in a modern design, set with random diamonds, the gold a mingling of red and yellow. For all that it was modern, there was a timeless quality about the ring that came from skilled workmanship, and Kirsty discovered that she was holding her breath as Drew took it from her and slid it deftly on to her finger.

It fitted as though it had been made for her, and in some strange way she felt as though it had.

'And then of course there's the wedding ring,' the jeweller was saying. 'Would you . . .'

Kirsty drew back in horror as she realised he wanted her to try it on.

'It's bad luck,' she protested weakly, knowing the excuse sounded foolish, but the jeweller seemed to understand, because he smiled, and said gently, 'Of course, we can leave it for now and then you could have it altered later. I'm sure it will fit.' And it was then that Kirsty realised that the ring was designed to fit snugly against the engagement ring, a final band of pale gold to tone in with the other two, the jagged edgings of both rings fitting perfectly together.

'I like to think it symbolic of the best of marriages,' the jeweller explained, 'a perfect dovetailing.'

'We'll take them both,' Kirsty heard Drew say, adding to her, 'You'll keep the engagement ring on, won't you, darling?'

She wanted to protest, but lacked the courage to make a scene in the small confines of the shop. Once outside it was a different matter, and she shrugged ineffectually at the offending band of gold which stubbornly resisted all her attempts to remove it.

'Leave it,' Drew commanded in far less lover-like tones than he had used before.

'Why?' she demanded. 'Surely Beverley isn't going to materialise out of nowhere to check that we're actually engaged? It takes more than a ring to turn two people into lovers.'

'I'm glad you realise it,' Drew mocked. 'But perhaps you're right,' he added thoughtfully. 'This . . .' he tapped the ring on her finger, 'isn't going to convince anyone for very long, if you persist in treating me like a stranger.'

'You are,' Kirsty reminded him, trying to pull away the hand he had retained and which he was proceeding to tuck through his arm.

'Is that so? Just how intimately do I have to know you before I cease to be?'

Kirsty stiffened at his side. 'You don't know me intimately at all,' she told him bitterly. 'Just my body.'

How it shamed her to add those last few words, but they couldn't be denied, nor his meaning ignored.

'Every delectable inch of it.'

He seemed bent on tormenting her; on reminding her subtly of her total abandonment to his lovemaking for those few brief seconds while sanity and caution had been suspended.

'I could have taken you then.'

The words seemed to shiver on the air between them.

'But without love,' Kirsty said painfully, her throat suddenly unbearably tight.

For a moment Drew seemed about to say something, and then someone bumped into them and the moment was gone, and with it the strange hurting sensation Kirsty had experienced.

Because there were no rehearsals in the afternoon, Drew had booked them a table at a restaurant just outside York.

'I would have suggested that we dine out

tonight,' he told her as they waited for their meal to be served, 'but I promised to go and see Simon. He wants to talk over various things with me.'

Simon must think a good deal of Drew's judgment and ability if he was content to leave so much in his hands, Kirsty acknowledged. She had discovered so much more about Drew since she had come to York; so many more facets to his personality.

'I didn't realise you wrote,' she murmured hesitantly, toying with the stem of her wine glass. 'Nor that you were Paul Bennett.'

'Why should you?'

For some reason the careless words hurt. 'I started writing some years ago—I acted for a while after leaving Oxford, but I grew bored with it. An actor needs total dedication, total belief in himself—that's something you must have already learned?'

It was, and deep in her heart of hearts, Kirsty didn't know if she was capable of such singlemindedness. Chelsea had sensed how she was and had sympathised with her. An actress often had to give up many things to be truly successful. Things like a happy marriage and a family, and Kirsty didn't know if she was capable of making such a sacrifice.

To banish her uncomfortable thoughts, she murmured, 'But you're a critic as well.'

'At the moment. It's not a role I particularly enjoy—As I said before, you have a very expressive face,' he told her. 'But it's true, I don't enjoy it, which is why I'm giving it up to concentrate more on working here and on my writing. I'm thirty—thirty-one almost; and I'm tired of living out of suitcases, of being a homeless nomad. I want to put down roots, have a family . . . call it a hang-up from my childhood if you like, but when I do I want it to be permanent. It might be selfish of me, but I'm not prepared to settle for anything less.'

Again she experienced the same curious pang she had felt earlier. Why should she care? she asked herself. Why should she feel pain at his admission of love for Beverley?

She barely tasted the steak in its delicious cream sauce, toying with the meat, wondering what had happened to her normally keen appetite.

It was late afternoon before they started back, and instead of taking her home, Drew drove her to the farmhouse. It was the first time she had seen it in daylight. It looked every bit as attractive as she had imagined, but this time she was able to catch her breath in awe at the magnificent views it commanded over the gently rolling countryside.

There was a car parked in the courtyard, and Drew frowned when he saw it.

Kirsty knew who it belonged to the moment she stepped into the hall. She could smell her perfume and recognised the heavy cloying scent of Opium, drowning out her own delicate application of Madame Rochas.

'Drew, darling—at last!'

'Beverley!'

His voice was as expressionless as his face, but

Beverley wasn't quite as adept at hiding her feelings, and bitter resentment showed in her eyes for a second as she saw Kirsty.

'Have I come at a bad time? Really, darling,' she smiled with false sweetness, 'I hadn't realised you were quite so impetuous!'

Drew shrugged aside the acid comment, only drawling, 'It's only natural that I should want to be alone with my new fiancée,' and Kirsty was sure it was by no mere accident that he caught up her hand, lifting it to his lips so that the light caught the diamond-studded gold ring.

However, it wasn't the ring she was thinking of, as she felt the warmth of his breath against her skin, his lips seductively probing her palm as he uncurled her fingers.

'Was it something important, Beverley?' he asked without lifting his eyes from Kirsty's face. 'Because if not . . .'

The tinkling laugh sounded as brittle as shards of glass to Kirsty's sensitive ears.

'Darling, you're hardly tactful,' Beverley complained. 'What I actually came here for was to return this.'

'This' was a key—the key she had used to unlock the door, Kirsty presumed, thus making it very plain that she had a perfect right to walk in and out of Drew's house whenever she chose. 'I shall hardly need it now,' she added pointedly.

Drew pocketed it without a word, but Kirsty was aware that he looked oddly pale beneath his tan, and she sensed that he was inwardly far from being as calm as he appeared as he escorted Beverley to the door and coolly closed it after her.

'She wanted me to know that she had a key to this house,' was all Kirsty could think of to say in the silence that followed the roar of her car's exhaust.

'You realise that, do you? Then we're making progress.' Beneath the sardonic tone, Kirsty sensed that he was bitterly angry, although she couldn't understand why. Surely the mere fact that Beverley had wanted her to know about the key proved that she was far from indifferent to him?

'You wanted to talk to me about Hero,' she reminded him hastily.

'Did I?' His mouth was wry. 'Somehow it had gone out of my mind. We'll talk about it another time, Kirsty,' he told her heavily. 'I've only got so much self-control, and I can't guarantee there's enough of it left to get us both unmaimed through even another hour together right now, so I'm going to take you home.'

He did so, in a silence that seemed thick with tension. What was he thinking about? Kirsty wondered, stealing a glance at his forbidding profile. Since they had returned from York he seemed to have changed; to have withdrawn into himself. Because Beverley had returned his key to him, no doubt, she thought tiredly. Her head ached, and she could hardly bear to glance at the glitter of gold and diamonds on her left hand. It seemed a sacrilege that such a beautiful thing should represent so hollow an alliance.

The Porsche came to a halt outside her bedsit. She tugged ineffectually at her seatbelt, shrinking when Drew pushed her hands away, cursing as he released it.

'Oh, for God's sake don't look at me like that!' he snapped harshly. 'You're supposed to be engaged to me, remember? Even timid virgins are allowed to look at their fiancés with something approaching desire—when you look at me it's either with fear or loathing. You're an actress, Kirsty,' he reminded her goadingly, 'and a good one, or so you tell me. Prove it to me now, and kiss me as though you were my fiancée!'

'Why?' she managed shakily. 'We haven't got an audience.'

'Ever heard of rehearsals?' Drew asked sardonically. 'And God knows, you need the practice.'

This last taunt was too much. Too furious to think logically, Kirsty slid her hands upwards over his chest, lifting her eyes to meet his.

'Good,' he told her, 'but not good enough. We're engaged, remember? We're already lovers, or so they think. And we're alone. I've just given you my ring. You're an actress, Kirsty, remember?'

And all at once she did. She wasn't Kirsty Stannard any longer, but the girl Drew had just described, free to experience all those weak, melting sensations curling insidiously through her stomach, sending her pulse rate sky-high as she lifted her hands to Drew's shoulders, caressing the smooth flesh-covered muscles, her lips trembling as she touched them to his throat, feeling the roughness of his jaw against her skin as his arms closed round her and his lips met hers in a kiss of sensual sweetness that swept aside all her preconceived ideas of what a kiss should be.

Certainly she had never, ever, experienced before this yielding tide of emotion; this need to press ever closer to Drew's body, her own moulding itself instinctively to his hardness, her fears forgotten in the headiness of what she was experiencing.

It wasn't until two boys cycled past the car, whistling appreciatively, that she came to, jerking herself out of Drew's arms with a shocked protest and wrenching open the car door before he could speak.

Acting! That was what she was supposed to have been doing, but only she knew how precious little acting ability it had taken to respond so passionately to Drew's touch.

The realisation came as she climbed the stairs to her room. She had fallen in love with Drew.

It ought to have been impossible, but somehow she had—against all the odds—managed it. She tried to convince herself that it wasn't true, that she was suffering from some strange delusion, but the truth once admitted would not be banished.

In the gathering dusk she sat completely motionless staring out of the window, trying to come to terms with the enormity of what had happened. Now more than ever before it was imperative that she got out of this fictitious engagement before Drew discovered the truth. It would be like being flayed alive, she thought helplessly. She couldn't endure it—no one could, not knowing all the time that he loved Beverley and was simply using her to punish Beverley and bring her to heel.

With almost feverish intensity she tried to formulate some sort of plan of escape.

The telephone rang. She picked up the receiver and heard Clive Richmond's voice on the other end.

'A few of us are getting together at my place to go over our parts. Do you fancy coming round? I'm providing the supper, visitors provide the booze. How about it?'

All at once it sounded just what Kirsty wanted—the same sort of uncomplicated, pleasant evening she had enjoyed so often at college.

'I'll be round in half an hour,' she promised, her spirits suddenly lightening. For this evening, she would put Drew and her love for him out of her mind.

It took her just over half an hour to reach the address he had given her. She had been delayed by Mrs Cummings whom she had met in the hallway, and had explained briefly to her where she was going.

Clive opened the door to her ring. Behind him Kirsty could see into the room, smaller and untidier than her own and lacking its cheerful warmth.

'Rafe and Cherry have just nipped down to the pub,' he greeted her, 'the others will be along shortly. Come on in.'

As far as Kirsty could see no attempts had been made to get any supper ready, and remembering her student days, she guessed that that task would fall to the girls when they all arrived.

Clive accepted the bottle of plonk she proffered and poured them both a glass.

'Make yourself at home,' he told her, gesturing to the lumpy settee taking up most of the room.

A dog-eared copy of the play had been tossed carelessly on to the floor, and Kirsty picked it up and started to read absently from it as Clive closed the curtains and turned off the main lights. With just the glow from the electric fire and the lamps behind them, the untidiness of the room looked less obvious. Clive put a tape in the cassette machine on the floor, and the sound of Dr Hook began to fill the room.

Kirsty listened appreciatively, making no objection when Clive joined her on the settee.

'How come you get such a juicy part, when a man of my many and varied talents only gets Borachio?' he demanded mock-indignantly.

Kirsty pretended to consider the matter, her head on one side, the dark richness of her curls flatteringly framed by the plum-coloured jumper she was wearing over her jeans. 'You're not pretty enough for Hero?' she ventured at last.

'And our revered director certainly doesn't fancy me,' he agreed. 'By the way, did you know he was dining with the Baileys tonight? And that Beverley was joining them?'

'I don't own him,' she managed at last, unwilling to admit to the searing jealousy she was experiencing. By the time tonight was over would Beverley be in possession of the key to Drew's house once more?

'He isn't worth it.' She realised that Clive was

watching her so closely. 'Besides, what's sauce for the goose . . .'

'Isn't it time the others started to arrive?' Kirsty asked to change the subject, glancing at her watch as she did so. 'It's getting quite late—there won't be much time left to do any work.'

'They'll be here soon,' Clive told her carelessly. 'And as for work, Drew will make sure none of us slack on that. I should have got Claudio,' he told her. 'My agent told me I'd as good as got the part, until your precious fiancé poked his nose in where it wasn't wanted, and told Simon he didn't think I'd got the experience. He obviously thinks you've got the experience,' he told Kirsty with a silky vehemence that sounded warning bells in her brain. 'Have you, Kirsty?'

'Not really.' She edged away from him.

'Oh, come on, don't give me that. Drew Chalmers is no fool. You can't be the little innocent you look. We could have fun together, you and I, Kirsty—you know that, don't you? We're two of a kind.'

Were they? Somehow Kirsty didn't think so. Cherry had warned her about Clive, but she had chosen to ignore her, thinking she could use him for her own ends. She had an uncomfortable feeling that she had bitten off more than she could chew. She didn't like the look in his eyes or the way he was smiling.

It came to her on a sudden rush of distaste that he expected her to cheat on Drew and that while he would do everything he could to encourage her, he was shallow and vain and totally without any substance for anyone to rely on. It was an unpleasant shock to realise how close she had been to allying herself to him, and she admitted tacitly that she would not now go through with her plan to use him to force Drew into abandoning their engagement. She would have to find another way; a way that did not leave her feeling as though she had failed her own high standards.

'I think I'd better be going,' she told him quickly. 'It's getting late, will you apologise for me to the others?'

'What others?' All at once the veneer of good humour was gone. 'Don't play games with me, Kirsty. We both know the ground rules. There never was anyone else—just the two of us, and that's the way we both wanted it, umm?' His fingers were moving up her arm as he spoke and Kirsty had to fight hard against a shudder of revulsion.

'You're wrong,' she told him firmly. 'I had no idea. I'm engaged to Drew—remember?'

She hated herself for the weak way she fell back on the protection of Drew's name; Drew's ring, glittering fierily on her finger.

'Sure I do,' Clive sneered. 'But we're both adults—you weren't thinking too much about Drew Chalmers on Sunday afternoon. Come on, Kirsty,' he wheedled, 'what's the harm?'

'The harm is that I'm engaged to someone else,' Kirsty told him. 'I'm sorry, Clive, but I honestly thought the others would be here.' She got up as she spoke, heading for the door, but Clive was there before her, his expression bitter as he grasped her arms, swinging her round to face him.

'You're a cheat, Kirsty.' There was an ugly look in his eyes, and a frisson of fear shot through her. 'But no one cheats me!'

Kirsty struggled to avoid the angry pressure of his mouth, flinching as he lost his temper with her, bruising the soft skin of her face as she tried to avoid his blow. He released her almost immediately, eyes narrowed as she trembled convulsively in front of him.

'Don't try running to Drew Chalmers with this,' he warned her softly. 'I'll tell him that you came here of your own free will. It's surprising how easily soft skin bruises—as I'm sure he already knows.' His mouth twisted mockingly, and Kirsty was not surprised to discover that she was still trembling when she reached her car.

She seemed to have matured immeasurably in a short handful of hours; first the discovery of her love for Drew, and then learning that sometimes safety came at too high a price. Her own self-respect refused to allow her to stoop to Clive Richmond's level, and she knew she would rather endure a thousand engagements to Drew in preference to encouraging Clive to believe that she would welcome a sordid affair with him behind Drew's back.

She inspected her face in her driving mirror before driving off. The skin along her cheekbone was already discolouring. There was a scratch on her throat just above the line of her jumper—she remembered tugging at it—and her bottom lip looked swollen and sore. Swallowing her distaste, she wished she had brought some make-up with her, but she rarely wore more than a touch of eyeshadow, mascara, and lip-gloss, and it would take more than those to disguise her bruises. At least she would be able to conceal them before she had to face the others at rehearsal tomorrow. Heavens, she was a fool! She might have guessed that Clive had no intention of asking the others. No wonder he had refused to believe her!

She did her best during the drive back to compose herself, but it wasn't easy. She wasn't going to overreact and assume that Clive had deliberately meant to hurt her, but she had found the experience both humiliating and degrading, and she had probably learned a valuable lesson from it, she admitted wryly, as she parked her car and slid her key into the lock.

Although it wasn't particularly late the house was in darkness apart from the single lamp glowing in her window, which she had left switched on when coming out. Mrs Cummings, she remembered, had said she was going out to visit her sister.

Never had the thought of the solitude of her own room been so welcome. She intended to have a bath and then go straight to bed. She was completely drained both mentally and physically.

Her door opened smoothly as she inserted her key, and she stepped into the small foyer. Her bruised face had started to throb painfully and she felt grubby and contaminated somehow by the ugly scene she had experienced. She would not be so naïve another time, and she certainly intended to give Clive Richmond a wide berth from now on.

She pushed open the door and stepped into the

warm pool of light cast by the lamp, freezing to the spot as Drew uncoiled his lean frame from her settee.

'Mrs Cummings let me in,' he told her calmly, his expression suddenly changing as he saw her face. 'My God, what. . . .'

'I don't want to talk about it,' Kirsty told him jerkily. 'Please leave. I don't know what you're doing here anyway. Clive told me that Beverley was visiting the Baileys tonight.'

'*Clive* told you?' He pounced, a bitterly cynical expression in his eyes as he looked again at her bruised face. 'And Clive did this to you, did he? A rough lover, I take it!'

The contempt in his eyes was like a lash on already torn skin, but Kirsty refused to give in to the weak desire to burst into tears, instead saying challengingly, 'And what if he is? What business is it of yours?'

He reached for her hand before she could stop him, turning it palm down so that the lamplight glittered on her ring.

'I should have thought this made it pretty much my business,' he told her, indicating the ring, 'and the fact that Clive chose to ignore it is hardly a good character reference—just the opposite. He's the type of man who enjoys stealing from others.'

His assessment was so correct that she was left speechless.

'Did he, Kirsty?' Drew demanded harshly, the tone of his voice demanding a response.

'If you're referring to me, he could hardly "steal" what doesn't belong to you,' Kirsty reminded him. She was about to tell him that the could hardly care what her relationship with Clive was, when he stunned her by saying softly,

'Then perhaps it's time it did.'

With two strides he had closed the gap between them, and Kirsty was being crushed against the wall of his chest, his voice grating against her ear as he muttered savagely, 'If it's physical violence that turns you on, try this for size!' And then his mouth was grinding down on hers, savaging the tender flesh as she struggled impotently in his arms.

CHAPTER SEVEN

BRIEFLY, Kirsty saw their reflections in the uncurtained window, Drew, tall and powerful, his body enveloping her smaller frame, intimacy cloaking their real emotions.

'Drew, don't do this,' she begged, dragging her mouth free from the assault of his, but he wasn't listening to her. His eyes were fastened on the small tear in her sweater, the expression in this turning her blood to ice, fear, freezing her muscles as he lifted his eyes to her face.

'Drew, it wasn't like that . . .' she protested, but he didn't seem to hear her.

'And to think I fell for that sweet, innocent act!' he muttered thickly. 'But you aren't innocent any more, are you, Kirsty?' He touched her mouth, probing with one finger, a cynical smile curving his mouth as she winced from the pain of her bruised flesh, trying to find the words to convince him that he was wrong. He was like a leashed animal in the small confines of her room, and the pent-up bitterness of his fury frightened her; all the more so because there was no reason for it.

The only possible objection he could have to her being with Clive was on the grounds of their supposed 'engagement', which they both knew to be fictitious, and his rage was as irrational as her jealousy had been when she discovered he was with Beverley Travers. Only her jealousy had a sound basis—she loved him, while he felt nothing at all for her.

She glanced nervously towards him and amended her thoughts. He did feel something for her. It was glittering in his eyes, etched into the cynicism of his face, and her stomach churned desperately as she recognised desire burning behind the cool façade. But why, and why now?

Was it because he thought she was no longer a virgin? Kirsty shuddered, cast adrift on an unfamiliar sea, longing for a known landmark to cling to, but they had all been swept away, just as Drew was threatening to sweep away her fragile defences.

'To think I denied myself because I thought I hadn't the right to destroy your innocence! Well, I'm not going to deny myself any longer. Do you know how long I've been sitting there there waiting for you to come back from your lover's arms? Over two hours,' he told her bitingly.

'I didn't know you were coming round,' Kirsty protested, trying to squirm out of his grasp. 'Clive told me he was having a party ...' She flushed, biting her lip. She hadn't intended to let that slip; she had no wish for Drew to mock her naïveté, but she needn't have worried, because it was obvious that he didn't believe her.

'Some party!' he grated. 'And it's not over.'

Kirsty grasped his forearms protestingly as he reached for the edge of her sweater.

'Drew, no!' she protested huskily. 'You have no right to ...'

'No right? Haven't you forgotten this?' he asked silkily, touching her ring. 'This gives me some pretty formidable rights these days, Kirsty, and this time I'm going to take them; even if it is rather late in the day. Perhaps I ought to thank Clive after all,' he added with cruel emphasis. 'Virgins don't exactly make exciting partners . . .'

Kirsty closed her eyes in mute protest at the cynicism of both his words and his expression. He made it sound so clinical and cold; not how she had imagined things at all—especially not with her very first lover, and all at once she had the icy conviction that Drew was going to be her first lover. She could read the determination in his hard mouth; the grip of his hands on her hipbones where her jumper ended.

'Fight all you want, Kirsty,' he breathed smokily as she tried to evade him. 'We both know what the eventual outcome will be, but if playing the unwilling victim is what turns you on, you go right ahead—just don't expect me to play along with you. But first . . .' His hands gripped her jumper, Kirsty stilling instinctively as she saw the banked-down rage in his eyes.

'Either you take this thing off, or I rip it off you piece by piece,' he said softly. 'And Kirsty,' he added as she stood like a wooden doll and he stripped the jumper from her, 'don't ever wear it in my presence again.'

'What's wrong with it?' Kirsty managed with a shaky flippancy. 'Don't you like the colour?'

'What I don't like is the way it makes me feel,' he told her enigmatically, 'but right now all I want to concentrate on is the way you make me feel. You're a very desirable female, Kirsty—but then of course you already know that, don't you?'

His hands rested on her rib cage, just below the soft thrust of her breasts, clearly marked with the beginnings of bruises where Clive had touched her. Drew splayed his own hand across her breast, obliterating the faint marks, and a tremulous, uncertain sensation spread upwards, dispelling the ice in her veins. Dear God, what was the matter with her? Kirsty wondered. After the way he had just spoken to her she should be loathing Drew, and yet her pulses leapt in undeniable response to his touch.

'You want me, Kirsty,' he murmured against her ear. 'Don't bother denying it. It's been there between us all along.'

'Perhaps I do,' Kirsty admitted, trying to conceal the shimmer of tears in her eyes, 'but that doesn't mean that I don't loathe myself for doing so.'

His response was to tighten his arms around her, his lips burning a fiery trail against her sensitive flesh, strong teeth nibbling at the tautly responsive cord in her throat, until she could feel her resistance slipping away like an ebb tide, leaving her stranded and vulnerable.

Of their own accord her fingers twined themselves in the night-darkness of Drew's hair, small sighing sounds of pleasure escaping her lips as his fingers moved over her collarbone and downwards, stroking over her skin, until it was dry and burning with fire to know his touch more intimately.

She wasn't even aware of his fingers deftly

unfastening her bra; only the thrilling surge of pleasure as the brief garment fell away and Drew's hands cupped her overheated flesh, caressing and soothing its burgeoning arousal. Soft and pliant as a kitten, Kirsty wound her arms round him, pressing her body close to the rigid masculinity of Drew's, gasping in sudden awareness of his arousal as his hands tightened on her hips, making no secret of the powerful thrust of male muscles.

Their quarrel, and all his insults, were forgotten, every sensitive nerve in Kirsty's body responding to Drew's skilled caresses. She wasn't aware of them moving to her bedroom, or of Drew carrying her to the bed, until he was lying full length on it beside her, his eyes feasting on the unexpected voluptuousness of her body. His hands encircling her waist, a deeply absorbed expression in his eyes as they moved slowly over her skin until she couldn't stop the softly pleading, 'Don't!' which escaped her lips.

'There's no reason to be shy now.'

For some reason he sounded more sad than angry, and Kirsty sensed that the bitterness which had driven him had given way to the same irresistible pull of pleasure she was experiencing. 'It's a very pleasurable sensation to have your body admired by your lover,' Drew told her in a deeply sensual voice. His thumb was probing the trembling curve of her mouth, and her bruises were forgotten as she tensed on a spiral of urgent excitement.

'Drew, I . . .'

'Go ahead,' he told her huskily, reading her

mind. 'You don't have to ask permission. In fact . . .'

A shiver of pleasure touched her skin as Drew removed first his sweater and then the checked shirt he was wearing underneath. In the dim glow from the lamp in the other room Kirsty could see the warm gold of his flesh, still tanned from time spent abroad. Dark hairs matted his chest, arrowing downwards, drawing her eyes wonderingly over his body to widen and gaze, confused, at the buckle of his belt.

'If you keep looking at me like that, Kirsty, you'll have to do more than just look,' Drew growled against her throat, 'and soon,' he concluded suggestively.

'Drew . . .'

'Don't talk, Kirsty, just feel, like this,' he told her urgently, possessing her mouth hotly, and depriving her of breath. Her hands moved instinctively over his skin, thrilling to the sensation of silk-sheathed muscle and sinew, contracting beneath her delicate exploration. Her lips, released from the intoxicating dominance of Drew's, made shy forays against his skin, tasting the male-scented flesh, revelling in the heady experience of feeling Drew's passionately urgent response, shyness and doubt swept aside in the avalanche of feeling that swept her as she felt Drew's skin beneath her lips. She wanted to go on and on touching and tasting, exploring the intoxicatingly alien maleness. Her fingers curled impotently into the waistband of his jeans, in sudden shock.

'What's the matter?' Drew's lips trailed

seductively over the curves of her breasts, his hands gripping her hips as he held her firmly against him. 'For God's sake, Kirsty,' he muttered hoarsely, 'what are you trying to do to me—drive me out of my mind? Help me get these damned jeans off. I want to feel you against me,' he added huskily. 'All of you.'

The sight of his naked body made her catch her breath in awe. Muscles rippled silkily beneath his skin as he moved, tall and powerfully built, his body that of a perfectly formed athlete.

'You're looking at me as if I'm the first naked man you've ever seen,' Drew taunted softly, 'and it's doing dangerous things to my self-control. I wanted to hurt you tonight, Kirsty,' he told her, 'but somehow all the anger's gone, and all I want to do right now is to make love to you until there simply isn't room for anything else but that. You're beautiful, Kirsty, every single bit of you.' He bent his head and a shaft of exquisite pleasure shot through her as his tongue touched provocatively against the aroused centre of her nipple, stroking and caressing until she was on fire with a heated need to know a more satisfying possession, gratified only when Drew's mouth eventually closed possessively over the aroused peak, pleasure almost too great to be borne boiling up inside her like a whirlpool.

Drew's ardent possession of her breasts swept away the last of her reserve, and Kirsty stopped fighting her growing desire to yield to her need to touch and caress him as intimately as he was touching her. The light kisses she pressed against the burning heat of his skin evoked a response that overwhelmed her, Drew choosing to show her how far along the paths of sensuality she still had to go, by tracing kisses over the gentle swell of her stomach, devastating her with the intimacy of his touch.

'Drew!'

She writhed wantonly against him, moaning faintly with pleasure as he moved against her, sliding between her thighs, his hands cradling her hips so that she arched instinctively against him, inciting his possession, relishing the fierce possession of his mouth buried against hers, the urgent thrust of his body against her, coiling her stomach muscles in nervous anticipation.

Some childlike impulse made her squeeze her eyes tightly closed, although she didn't realise how painfully her fingernails were biting into Drew's back, until he relinquished her mouth to murmur protestingly in her ear, 'Relax!'

She tried to do as she said, letting herself slide down into the sensual fever racing through her blood, not making any attempt to combat her urgent need for his possession. She loved him, and instinct told her this might be the only time they would share such intimacy. Dimly she knew that she ought to be resisting; ought to be reminding herself that Drew didn't love her, but with the rough pressure of his long legs against hers, her breasts crushed against the warmth of his chest, the fierce thud of his heartbeat drowning out her own and the feverish thrust of his body as desire overwhelmed him it was impossible to think of anything but the heady pleasure of here and now.

'Drew. Drew . . .' His name left her lips on a whispered litany, her head moving restlessly from side to side. His hands shaped her face, holding it captive as he plundered her mouth, taking all that she gave in sweet surrender and still demanding more until she was lightheaded with pleasure.

'I want you, Kirsty,' Drew muttered thickly against her mouth. 'So much that I don't even care any more that . . .' He checked swiftly as a small gasp of pain escaped her, drawing away to stare down into her flushed face. 'Kirsty?'

She turned away childishly, closing her eyes.

'Kirsty, you aren't . . . Clive didn't make love to you, did he?' he demanded softly, forcing her to look at him. 'My God,' he muttered under his breath. 'God, what have I done?' He spoke more to himself than to her, and Kirsty watched him with huge hurt eyes as he moved away from her, sitting on the edge of the bed with his back to her as he bent to retrieve his jeans.

'Does it matter whether or not Clive has made love to me?' she managed at last, feeling exposed and vulnerable, lying on the bed beside him. 'Does it make any difference?'

'All the difference in the world,' Drew told her tersely without looking at her. 'God, surely I don't need to tell you that!' He turned and she flinched from the look of bitter loathing in his eyes, scorched with the humiliation of knowing that he was rejecting her.

He had wanted her—he had told her so; but now, suddenly, he didn't. Because he had discovered that she was after all still a virgin. What difference did that make? All the difference in the world, Kirsty acknowledged. Drew wouldn't want the responsibility of taking her virginity—or the possible consequences. He loved Beverley Travers; she already knew that. All he had felt for Kirsty had been desire—and now that desire was gone.

She refused to look at him as he dressed, tensing as she felt him stand up and then bend over her.

'Kirsty . . .'

'Please go,' she begged in a curt little voice. She couldn't bear his pity. It was bad enough that she had been on the point of giving herself to him without love, without her having to endure his pity. 'We've nothing left to say to one another, Drew.'

She hadn't realised she had been holding her breath until she heard the sound of the front door closing behind him. He was gone. She lay on her bed for several seconds, simply staring at the door, and then the tears came, a mingling of reaction and pain.

She loved him, and she had given him the most precious gift she had to give. He had rejected that gift, and the knowledge brought a searing pain, so intense that it overrode everything else.

The moment Kirsty opened her eyes in the morning she remembered what had happened. She was trembling when she left the house to go to rehearsal. How on earth was she going to face Drew? By the time she reached the theatre she was a tense bundle of nerves. She parked her car without her normal care, forcing a smile to her lips as she walked on to the stage to join those who were already gathered there.

Rachel and David were deep in conversation, Pete, the lighting technician, was busily engaged working on some of the footlights. There was no sign of Cherry, and Kirsty drifted over to a group which included Meg and Chris. She had already seen Clive and was sure that he had seen her, although he had pretended not to.

'It came as quite a shock to Simon, I can tell you,' Meg was saying, 'and poor Helen is terribly disappointed—but then of course he really had no choice.'

'He's gone, then?'

'Oh yes,' Meg agreed. 'First thing this morning. Poor you,' she sympathised with Kirsty. 'Have you any idea when he'll be back?'

Kirsty tried not to look too baffled, heaving a quick sigh of relief as Simon suddenly walked in, greeting them with a rather preoccupied smile.

'I expect most of you know by now that Drew has had to return to London—some problem with a script he's been working on, but let's hope he should be back before too long. Today,' he continued briskly, 'I want to concentrate on Claudio and Hero's roles, so if Kirsty and Rafe could both come over here.'

Drew gone! Kirsty could barely take it in. Surely he had not left because of last night? But no, Simon had said something about a script. She tried to comfort herself with the knowledge that Drew would never react so emotionally to what had happened, but the niggling suspicion that he had left rather than work with her could not be completely obliterated.

As the morning wore on and she became more engrossed in her role, she was able to push Drew to the back of her mind.

They broke for lunch, Kirsty accepting Rafe's suggestion that they eat together at the local pub. They spent most of the time discussing their parts and by the time they returned to the theatre, to watch Simon taking Rachel and David through their roles as Beatrice and Benedick, she was feeling a lot calmer.

That calm was shattered when Simon announced that they had worked hard enough for one day, and Rachel came over towards her.

'So Drew's back in London,' she murmured, eyeing Kirsty speculatively. 'My poor darling— but then, of course, it was on the cards right from the word go that your engagement couldn't last. Drew's a worldly, sophisticated man, who allowed his desire to outweigh common sense; something I'm sure he's regretting now. After all,' she pointed out with sweet malice, 'if he had really wanted to, there's nothing to stop him working on the script down here.'

The days took on a routine pattern; Simon was an excellent director, who knew how to get the best out of his actors. Rachel made an excellent Beatrice, Kirsty acknowledged, watching her one afternoon as she and David rehearsed the opening scenes of the play. On stage she underwent a transformation that enabled her to become Beatrice, and Kirsty envied her it. Rachel was singleminded about her profession in a way that she could never be, she acknowledged. Her husband had extensive business interests and neither of them seemed to mind the separation. Perhaps she was not cut out to be an actress after all, she reflected, as Simon took her on one side to explain exactly what he wanted from her as Hero.

'Traditionally Hero readily forgives Claudio for renouncing her, but both Drew and I want to see her behave with a little more spirit. That speech when Claudio rejects her during the wedding ceremony, for instance, we want you to inject more sarcasm than pathos into it. You are being rejected by the man you love; initially you are confused and defensive, but then . . .' He spoke several of Hero's lines to indicate what he meant, and several other members of the cast drifted over to listen as Rafe and Kirsty went through the scene again.

'You're getting the hang of it,' Simon approved, glancing at his watch. 'I just want to run through your final scene,' he told the two men playing Don Pedro and Don John, and as Kirsty turned away Rachel came up to her.

'Very good,' she praised. 'But then of course you'll be quite familiar with rejection, won't you? Have you heard from Drew since he went to New York?'

Kirsty tried to conceal her shock, and knew she had failed when Rachel murmured with exaggerated and entirely fictitious concern, 'Oh, my dear, didn't you know? He and Beverley flew out there together two days ago. She rang me from New York last night—she was over the moon . . .'

It was after that that Kirsty stopped wearing
Drew's ring, relinquishing her last, faint hope
that a miracle might occur and that he might
suddenly come to care for her. Cherry commented
on its absence, and Kirsty explained it away by
saying that the ring was a little large and she was
afraid of losing it.

Helen came to watch them rehearse one
afternoon, and Kirsty was shocked to see how
pale and tired she looked. That Simon was
concerned about her too was obvious, and Kirsty
felt an irrational shaft of resentment against
Drew. Couldn't he even spare a couple of weeks
from Beverley's side to relieve his friend of the
burden of directing the play? But then lovers
were inclined to be selfish, she admitted, and she
wondered how long she would have to wait
before she could tactfully allow it to be known
that their 'engagement' was over. She didn't want
to say anything while Helen was looking so ill;
Helen had already asked her several times if she
had heard from Drew, mentioning that she knew
how much she must be missing him, and how
pleased they were about their engagement, and
Kirsty had no wish to upset her by announcing it
was over.

The days spread into weeks. Gradually the
play started to come together. Costumes arrived
and were fitted; scenery was made ready, and an
indefinable but noticeable tension began to grip the
cast, adding a sharp, zestful edge to rehearsals.

Only Kirsty seemed unable to share the
growing excitement. She was conscious of a
certain lack of something in her own perfor-

mance that bothered her and made her feel that she was letting Simon down. If he was aware of it, he didn't say so, but Rachel's constantly expressed doubts about the changing of Hero's traditional role nibbled away at her self-confidence, and Kirsty felt sure that it was no accident that the other woman often contrived to be in the vicinity when they were rehearsing. Twice she had dropped props; on one occasion she had broken into a coughing spasm and on another she had dislodged a piece of scenery just as they were building up to the crux of the wedding scene.

Had they been acting in front of an audience, Kirsty had no doubt that she could have accused Rachel of deliberately trying to distract their attention, but it was impossible to suggest that the older and infinitely more experienced actress was trying to throw her off balance, and anyway, Kirsty didn't feel that she wanted to descend to Rachel's petty level.

Even so, she was finding the strain tiring, and confided her fears to Cherry one evening as they walked towards the car park together.

'I'm sure you're wrong,' Cherry comforted her, when Kirsty told her how worried she was about her portrayal of Hero's role. 'Simon is very pleased with you, I know, although he's a bit preoccupied at the moment, poor love. The hospital want Helen to go in on an in-patient basis until after the birth, but she won't hear of it. Any idea when Drew's coming back?'

'He's in New York at the moment,' Kirsty told her, trying not to let her voice betray her.

'Umm. It's a terrible shame that that script business should have come up right now, but then I don't suppose he had much option, not if he was already contracted, but you must miss him dreadfully.'

Someone Kirsty managed a monosyllabic response, and only she knew how bitterly true it was. She did miss him, with a dull, nagging ache that gave her an insight into what she was going to have to endure for the rest of her life.

All her normal optimism and exuberance seemed to have been quenched; she felt quenched herself, muted and dull, as though loving Drew had destroyed her vivacity and joie de vivre. She was tempted to go home for a weekend, but dreaded her parents reading the truth in her face, she had changed so much. If nothing else, knowing Drew had forced her into adulthood, and she had left behind for ever the girl who had so glibly decided to punish him for daring to criticise her.

Even now she found it impossible to remember the feel of his skin and the warmth of his mouth without aching to experience both again.

Lying sleepless at night, she sometimes endured the unbearable torture of re-living the sensation of being in his arms, but the experience was too painful and she had taken to sitting up, either reading or working, until she was on the point of exhaustion, solely to ensure that when she went to bed she would sleep.

CHAPTER EIGHT

'DON'T worry—you always think you're far worse than you actually are. It's a well known actor's failing,' Rafe comforted Kirsty, as he helped her down from the stage.

They had just finished a pre-dress rehearsal run-through, and compared with the polished performances of the others, Kirsty was convinced that her own fell very far short of their expertise.

'For what it's worth I think Simon is right, and you're bringing a freshness to Hero that's very winning. David thinks so too,' he added with a wicked grin. Although professionally their Beatrice and Benedick could not be faulted, there had been a few sparks flying between the two leading actors, which Kirsty found a little surprising because David had always had a reputation for being an extremely unprecious actor, with an extremely even temperament. Rachel had tried to upstage him, and while he had not allowed her attitude to provoke him into a quarrel, he had been firm and direct about making sure the incident wasn't repeated. Cherry had confided to Kirsty that Simon wasn't too happy with the actress either, although he admitted that she made an excellent Beatrice.

'I'm afraid I'm never going to be anything even approaching as good as Rachel,' Kirsty told him honestly.

'Would you want to be?' David raised his eyebrows and looked down at her. 'Surely once you're married to Drew acting will take something of a second place in your life—unless of course I've misread your character.'

Kirsty shook her head.

'No, I'll never have the dedication to devote my whole life to it.'

'That's just as well,' David laughed. 'I can't see Drew being too happy about that. Heard anything from him recently?' he added casually.

How much had he heard? Kirsty wondered numbly. There had been a time when Rachel had made no secret of the fact that, married or not, she couldn't be entirely averse to allowing their mutual roles to extend beyond the boundaries of Shakespeare's play, and even though now she was barely civil to David when they weren't on the stage, Kirsty couldn't be sure that she hadn't told him about Beverley and about her being in New York with Drew.

'He writes,' she lied eventually, 'but . . .'

'Letters are never an adequate recompense?' he suggested with a faint smile. 'If I didn't know that in my heart of hearts I'd be poaching, I'd suggest that you have dinner with me tonight, Kirsty. 'He added with a wry smile, 'Drew's a very lucky man. Girls like you are all too thin on the ground these days.'

'Thank you, kind sir,' Kirsty managed with a shaky grin. The mere mention of Drew had been sufficient to awaken all the anguish she had fought to put behind her since he had gone.

'What's going on here?' They had been

standing together in the shadows offstage, and Rachel's acidly sneering remark and searching gaze made them both move slightly away. 'Private tuition?' she goaded in the same sour tone. 'I hope you benefit from it, my dear—you can certainly do with it, but then of course I tend to forget that you don't have the experience of the rest of us. At least not on stage,' she added insultingly. 'What was it now—two flops behind you?'

'One, actually.' Kirsty was proud of the quiet calmness of her voice because she was feeling far from calm.

'Bitch!' David remarked succinctly as Rachel pushed past them. 'I hope she doesn't use this to make trouble between you and Drew,' he added.

'I doubt if anything she had to say would alter Drew's feelings towards me,' Kirsty told him lightly. It was, after all, probably the truth. Drew's opinion of her was already so low, it couldn't possibly sink any lower, and then, although David didn't know it, telling him that she had found them together was hardly to evoke any response. She was wearing Drew's ring again. Somehow she hadn't been able to resist the temptation to wear it, and she fingered it now with a prescient feeling of sadness. How long would it be before she no longer had any rights, however tenuous, to what it symbolised?

Simon had already told her that Drew was having to stay in New York longer than he had planned. Why? Because Beverley was there and he couldn't bear to be parted from her? Asking herself such painful questions was a profitless exercise, and when Cherry suggested that she join them at the pub across the road from the theatre for a drink before going their separate ways, Kirsty agreed.

Everyone apart from her seemed to be in an effervescent mood. The rehearsals were going well, or so the others seemed to think

Rafe, who was playing Claudio to her Here, sat next to her questioning her about her views of Simon's interpretation of her part.

'I must say I think it's working very well,' he told her enthusiastically. 'It was Drew's idea originally, of course. He told me about it when they were initially auditioning for *Much Ado*. I remember I asked him then who was playing Hero, and he told me he hadn't found her. He wanted someone special, he said, someone who could rise above the traditional playing of the role. In fact I seem to remember that he expressed a good deal of admiration for Hero,' he added with a grin. 'Something about her being a much easier woman to live with than Beatrice with all her fireworks. It looks as if he really meant it,' he added slyly. 'Have the two of you named the big day yet?'

Kirsty was saved from answering when Meg started to tell her about the time she had played Hero, and how difficult she had found it.

Kirsty had the impression that they were all, in their separate ways, trying to build up her self-confidence, and her despondency grew. She was not right for the part, she knew it. She lacked the experience, the verve, Simon was looking for. She would let him and the others down, she knew she would.

'Don't forget, everyone, dress rehearsal Wednesday,' Simon reminded them as he got up to leave. 'I've got to run now, Helen hasn't been feeling too good. No rehearsals tomorrow—have a day off.' There was a chorus of groans because it had been over a week since they had a full day off, Simon had been working them and himself hard, and Kirsty had been glad of it. She had returned to her bedsit in the evenings too tired to do anything other than fall into bed, but now she was going to have a full day of leisure, with nothing to do but think about Drew and worry about their opening night. And she was worried. Far more worried than she had been with either of her two previous parts. All at once she couldn't understand why she had ever wanted to go on the stage, and on impulse when she got home, she dialled Chelsea's number in Northumberland

Her aunt's husky, warm tones had an immediate soothing effect on her frayed nerves. She listened in silence as Kirsty poured out all her woes, although she was careful to make no mention of Drew.

'I wish you had more than one day off,' Chelsea complained. 'You could have come up to us. I was speaking to your mother last night, she's worried about you.' In Northumberland Kirsty imagined Chelsea grinning sympathetically. Both of them had suffered in their time from Ann Stannard's mothering tendencies, and Ann was inclined to be rather proud of the fact that she had been instrumental in bringing Chelsea and her husband Slade together.

'Try not to worry, Kirsty,' Chelsea told her. 'I

wish I could see you—it's so frustrating only being able to talk. You don't sound the same somehow. I have the feeling something's changed, but I don't know what. *Are* you all right?'

'Fine,' Kirsty assured her brightly. 'I've just grown up, that's all,' and then she rang off quickly before Chelsea could ask any more questions.

'Oh, Kirsty, you look absolutely fantastic! Your waist's so tiny!' Cherry enthused, perched on a stool in the crowded, hot dressing room, watching them all struggle into their costumes.

Hers was very attractive, Kirsty owned. Of bright crimson taffeta with a soft cream under-skirt, it had originally been intended for Beatrice, but despite her dark wig, Rachel had categorically refused to wear the crimson, claiming that it destroyed her complexion.

'They're getting ready for first calls,' Cherry warned her. 'Oh, I always love the first dress rehearsal. Somehow when you see the play performed in costume for the first time it really comes alive. The scenery is fantastic too. It was clever of Drew to suggest that we use the local art school. They've certainly come up with some clever ideas.'

The art students had done an excellent job, under Pete's able direction. A familiar tension gripped Kirsty as she stepped on stage behind Rachel—and then she wasn't Kirsty Stannard any more; she was Hero, placid, good-natured cousin to the fiery, temperamental Beatrice, but beneath that placidness was resolution and courage, and those were the qualities that must show through to the audience, and it was up to her to make sure they did!

Leonato was speaking the opening lines, Geoff replying ably in his role as Messenger. Then it was Rachel's turn, quick-witted and faintly cruel as she asked after Benedick.

Leonato's, 'What is he that you ask for, niece?' was Kirsty's cue and she took a deep breath, her smile and demeanour calm and unruffled, but there was a twinkle in her eyes and a lilt to her voice as she said demurely, 'My cousin means Signior Benedick of Padua . . .'

After that the lines and acts followed one another in steady succession until just before the marriage scene where Claudio was to reject her. Kirsty came off stage to find everything in a complete uproar.

'Talk about the show must go on!' Cherry was muttering through clenched teeth, her expression lightening as she saw Kirsty. She grabbed hold of her and pulled her into the dressing room.

'Drew's on his way back,' she told her quickly.

'Drew? You mean from New York?' Kirsty asked faintly. Her heart was pounding heavily, Hero completely forgotten.

'I mean from London, to here,' Cherry told her. 'It all blew up last night. Did you know Simon wasn't here?'

'Yes, someone said he'd been delayed.'

'Half right. Helen wasn't well all day yesterday, and then last night she had to be rushed into hospital. Simon rang Drew in New York, and he announced that he was coming back to take over so that Simon could be free to be with Helen. It's pretty serious,' Cherry added gravely. 'They may well have to induce, both for the baby's sake and Helen's, but I thought I'd just tell you. In all the panic I thought Drew might not have been able to let you know he's coming back. First available Concorde flight, and then an internal flight to York. He should be here soon. Simon told me that Drew said he wanted to be in time to catch the dress rehearsal if he could. Quick, you're back on,' Cherry added. 'I just thought I'd give you the good news—cheer you up a bit.'

Cheer her up! The thought of Drew witnessing her performance was enough to give Kirsty a severe case of tummy butterflies, but worse, far worse than that, was the thought of the inevitable confrontation when the rehearsal was over and she was forced to listen to him telling her that his plan had worked; that he and Beverley were back together, and that she in his role of 'fiancée' was no longer needed!

Somehow she managed to get back on stage, although she was barely aware of what was going on until Rafe started on Claudio's rejection speech. Had Drew arrived yet? Cherry in her role of A.S.M. was keeping an eye on proceedings, but it wasn't the same as having Simon there, and Kirsty could sense the production beginning to lose its sharp edge as the news of Helen's condition and Simon's absence began to filter through, and Simon's young assistant, Brian Felton, strived desperately to keep things going.

'Watch out for Rachel,' Cherry warned Kirsty when she came backstage to change. 'She's tried already to throw you off guard. If Simon were here she wouldn't stand a chance of getting away with it.'

'Any news about Helen?' Kirsty asked as the dresser used the hidden Velcro fastening to snap her second gown closed.

'Only that they're still waiting—Simon rang while you were on stage. He wanted to know if Drew had arrived.'

'You know what this means, don't you?' Rafe muttered to Kirsty as they waited to go back on stage. 'Another dress rehearsal almost straight away. I don't know why Simon simply didn't cancel today's. God knows how they moved in all this gear!'

Kirsty smiled, but her heart wasn't really in it. She was too keyed up and tense.

She made several small slips in the lead up to the wedding scene, forcing herself to listen to Rafe's rich baritone as he started to denounce her. This was almost her most important part of the play, and her hands had gone icy cold with dread. She started to speak, her voice, low but carrying, forcing herself to concentrate on Hero's shocked disbelief. She had barely started the speech when she was distracted by a small commotion off stage, and she didn't need to turn her head to look fully at the man striding towards them, commanding her to stop, to know who it was.

'No, Kirsty, that's not right,' she heard him saying crisply, and then he was facing her, looking surprisingly fresh after his long journey, in a plaid shirt open at the throat, his dark hair unruly.

'You're too passive,' he told her. 'At this stage you're still unable to believe what you've just heard, still unable to accept what's happening, and your voice must convey that to the audience. Outwardly your protest is contained, but inwardly, you can't endure the agony of hearing Claudio denounce you. You thought he loved you. How can he believe such terrible things about you? You must have fallen in love as a teenager. Try to recapture the emotion you felt then, the agony of losing that first love. It can't have been so very long ago . . .'

'Think about how you would feel if you lost Drew,' Rachel suggested silkily, and even though she knew Rachel was waiting and watching for her response, Kirsty couldn't prevent herself from going white. She had lost him already, and her pain *was* unendurable.

Somehow she managed to get through the scene, doing as Drew instructed, trying to blot out the reality of his presence and concentrate instead on his instructions. The difference was immediately noticeable; the entire play took on a new sharpness. During a brief respite between scene Kirsty learned that Drew had phoned the hospital.

'Helen is responding better to treatment than they expected,' he told Kirsty when she asked anxiously after Simon's wife. 'But they're still going to keep her in for observation for a few days anyway. Simon will stay with her, and I'll direct *Much Ado*.'

'But your work on the script?' Kirsty demurred.

'More or less finished, but even if it hadn't been, I was planning on coming home anyway. There's something I want to discuss with you.'

'I've got to go back,' Kirsty interrupted desperately. 'Cherry's waving to me.'

Despite all her efforts it was virtually impossible for her to concentrate after that. No matter how much she tried to throw herself into her role, Drew's words kept coming between her and the play. She no longer cared that Rachel was constantly trying to upstage her, using her more powerful role to either obscure her visually or destroy her concentration.

At last the play was reaching its close. Soon she would have to listen to Drew, would have to hear him saying that he and Beverley were back together and that his engagement to her could now be brought to an end.

Claudio's familiar lines accepting her as his bride in the place of the Hero he thought dead washed over her. Rafe was stepping towards her so that they could exchange the kiss Simon had decided was symbolic of their reunion. Kirsty stepped back as Rafe released her, preparatory to saying her final lines, and then suddenly Drew was on stage with them, ordering them to stop.

'Rafe, when you kiss Hero, you must initially do so hesitantly, reluctantly—after all, the woman you love is dead, and it's all your fault. As penance you've elected to marry another woman of her father's choosing, but you have no desire for the marriage. Your wife-to-be is not Hero. And yet, as you kiss her, your senses relate to you the fact that you're holding in your arms the woman you love, so before Hero removes her mask you're already saying wonderingly, "Another Hero . . ."

'And you, Kirsty,' he turned to Kirsty, 'you've told yourself that you'll marry Claudio to punish him; his shock is your sweet revenge, and yet when he kisses you, revenge is forgotten and you remember only that he's the man you love. I want you to communicate that to the audience.'

He made them run through the scene again, exclaiming with dissatisfaction when they played the final scene.

'No, you're not striking the right sparks off one another. When you kiss it's like watching two comfortable friends embracing. When you kiss Hero, and realise who she is, all your love and anguish must be in your face; you break the kiss reluctantly. Look, perhaps it will be easier if I show you what I want.'

Rafe moved aside, as Kirsty stared numbly up into Drew's face. He instructed the other actors to lead them in, approaching Kirsty with reluctance as he was shown his new bride-to-be by Antonio.

'Why, then she is mine.' The words were spoken wryly, with a faint edge of bitterness that faded to sorrowful acceptance as he continued. 'Sweet, let me see your face.' His fingers touched the mask she was wearing and Kirsty trembled to feel them against her face. Her skin felt hot and dry and she barely heard Leonato's lines, didn't even realise he had finished speaking until Drew took her hand. She had forgotten everyone else existed; forgotten that they were playing parts and was conscious of very little other than the powerful magnetism of his eyes on her face, his fingers stroking the vulnerable flesh of her inner wrist.

'I am your husband, if you like of me.'

It was her cue, and she raised her eyes to his, conscious of the warmth of his palm through her costume as he drew her against him, shaping her body to his as he kissed her, lightly, lifting his head to study her face with dawning incredulity before kissing her again.

Her mouth moved on hers softly, feeding her deep hunger, until in spite of all her efforts to resist him she was responding blindly. His hand slid into her hair, holding her captive, the pressure of his mouth increasing, no longer subtle, but hungrily demanding. Kirsty forgot that they were merely playing two parts. He was Drew, and she loved him. She was drowning in his kiss, taking pleasure from the hardness of his hands against her skin. She wanted it to go on and on for ever.

When he lifted his head she stared blindly up at him. He was speaking, and it was several seconds before she realised, humiliatingly, that he was speaking Claudio's lines.

When he had finished there was a spontaneous burst of applause from the onlookers, although Rafe did remark teasingly, 'Of course, the fact that you and Kirsty are engaged had nothing to do with the excellence of your performance!'

'It helped,' Drew admitted. He was watching Kirsty with an expression she could not decipher; a considering, almost yearning expression, but he moved and she decided it must have been a trick of the light, unless of course he had been thinking of Beverley alone in New York.

The scene came to an end and with it the play. Drew summoned them all together to run through what he had seen of the play, and as Cherry had suggested, announced that they would have another full dress rehearsal at the end of the week.

'So far, so good, from what I saw,' he told them, 'but there are several things that need brushing up. Your scene, Kirsty and Rafe, and also Rachel—your Beatrice is excellent, but occasionally you seem to forget that you're very fond of your cousin—it doesn't always come through.'

It was obvious that Rachel wasn't too pleased by the criticism. She opened her mouth to retaliate, but Drew had already moved on to another part.

Kirsty was exhausted by the time they had finished and she had changed back into her normal clothes. Cherry and several of the others were gathered in the foyer as she left, chatting about the rehearsal.

'We're off to the pub,' Rafe told her. 'Fancy coming with us?'

'She'd better not!' None of them had seen Drew emerge from the other side of the foyer, a supple cream leather jacket over his black pants and cashmere sweater. 'I've already got plans for tonight, and they don't include sharing her with anyone else!'

Everyone laughed, although Kirsty felt herself

colouring faintly. He wanted to talk to her, Drew had said, and she could guess what about. It was hardly likely to be the romantic reunion the others were doubtless thinking. Just for one weakening second she allowed herself to think of how it might have been if they were really engaged. Drew would have taken her back to the farmhouse, the tension in both of them growing until they were alone.

Once inside he would kiss her as he had kissed her earlier, and then . . .

She deliberately delayed until everyone else had gone, and then when they were alone, and Drew was holding open the door, she told him shakily, 'Drew, if you don't mind, I'd rather give it a miss tonight. It's been rather a long day . . .'

'You think I don't know that? You should try flying across the Atlantic and then you'd really know what a long day is. Where's your feminine compassion, Kirsty?' he demanded tauntingly. 'Is that the best you can do by way of a welcome home?'

'I'm sure it doesn't compare at all with Beverley's greeting,' Kirsty heard herself saying in a tightly bitter voice that filled her with dismay.

'Beverley is a woman,' Drew agreed, watching her sardonically, 'while you're still a child. When are you going to grow up, little girl? Come on, I'll take you home,' he finished abruptly.

He escorted her to his car in silence, driving competently the short distance to her bedsit. Fortunately she had walked to the theatre that morning, although she would had preferred driving home alone to sitting next to Drew in the unnerving silence that stretched her nerves to breaking point.

'Not quite the conclusion to the evening the others were visualising,' he drawled as he leaned across to open the door for her. 'It's not exactly idyllic from my point of view either,' he added with unkind cynicism.

Suddenly they seemed to be enemies. Perhaps he was annoyed because she hadn't asked him about Beverley. He was obviously missing her, but Kirsty felt far too heartsick herself to pander to his desire to talk.

As though he read her mind, he said curtly, 'We still have to have that talk, Kirsty, but it's obvious that neither of us is in the mood tonight. Having waited this long, I don't suppose it's going to kill me to wait a bit longer—I can't pretend I'm going to enjoy it, though!'

CHAPTER NINE

By rights tonight there shouldn't be anything on her mind other than the fact that this was their first night, Kirsty reflected, sliding into the car and closing the door. But there was something else on her mind. Drew! Since his return from New York the only times she had seen him had been during rehearsal and occasionally afterwards when he drove her home. During these drives he had been silent and preoccupied—thinking about Beverley, she had told herself, but if so, his thoughts could hardly be pleasant ones, if they were to account for the grim lines round his mouth and the look in his eyes.

He had never made any reference to the discussion he wanted to have with her, and Kirsty wondered if he was waiting until after their first night to break the news. Perhaps he had guessed how she felt about him, despite her pains to conceal it, and didn't want to upset her before the play opened. The play—she had thought Simon dedicated, but it was nothing to the energy Drew put into the production, and somehow that energy seemed to reach out to everyone involved, striking off sparks that lifted it from being merely good to being something exciting and different.

Cherry had seen it. She had told Kirsty

excitedly that it was the best production the
company had done.

'You make a fantastic Hero,' she praised, but
Kirsty knew that no matter how many times she
played the final scene with Rafe she would never
reach the heights she had done with Drew. Why
on earth had she been so stupid as to fall in love
with him in the first place? Hadn't she always
vowed that she would never fall in love until she
was in her twenties—at least twenty-six, she had
once told her aunt. How easy those words had
been to say; and how disastrously wrong!

Backstage all was chaos. Members of the cast
were hurrying in and out of dressing rooms,
demanding make-up and costumes; on stage Pete
was testing the lighting, and as she hurried to the
dressing room Kirsty could hear the scenery
being moved about on stage ready for the first
scene. Apprehension gripped her, panic sliding
coldly through her veins. What if she forgot her
lines? What if she missed a cue? She had felt like
this before, of course, but before she had not
been a member of such a prestigious cast. She
trembled as she remembered how bitchily Rachel
had commented on her inexperience the previous
day. The older woman seldom lost an opportunity
to remind her that Drew and Beverley had been
in New York together. She mustn't think of that
now, she told herself panickily as she stripped off
her jeans and sweater, pulling on a cotton gown
as she sat down to start on her make-up.
Fortunately, because she was already dark, unlike
Rachel she had no need of a wig.

Cherry came in as she was applying the thick

foundation needed to show up under the footlights.

'Guess what?' she demanded excitedly. 'The most fantastic news! Helen has had a little girl—this morning. They decided to do a Caesar last night, apparently. Simon's here—he came straight to the theatre from the hospital. He's over the moon, as you can imagine. They've decided to call the baby Hero, apparently—God help the poor little mite,' she added with a pious grin.

'Simon must be relieved that it's over,' Kirsty commented, applying eyeshadow. 'It must have been a dreadfully worrying time for him.'

'Yes, he looked exhausted when he walked in. He's going to stay for the performance. I left him talking with Drew. By the way,' Cherry asked Kirsty, 'how's Rafe? Is his throat any better?'

Rafe had developed a sore throat the previous day, and Kirsty had been concerned about him. Twice during one speech he had been on the verge of losing his voice completely, and Drew had advised him to rest it during the rehearsal.

'I haven't seen him yet. He's sharing a dressing room with David, isn't he? I'll go and find out how he is. Are you all ready for the party afterwards?'

Kirsty managed a weak smile. In truth she could not think beyond the performance to the party being held afterwards.

'I would be in your shoes,' Cherry told her. 'You've barely seen anything of Drew recently, apart from during rehearsal. Have you made any plans yet—for the wedding, I mean?'

'We haven't talked about anything other than

the play,' Kirsty told her truthfully, grateful for the warning bell ringing stridently to remind them how close they were to curtain-up.

'Well, there's one good thing,' Cherry told her as she opened the door to leave. 'The seats are filling up very nicely—you know we've sold all the tickets? We normally do very well on first nights, but this time we've surpassed ourselves—will your family be there?'

Kirsty managed a noncommittal shrug. To tell the truth she was both disappointed and hurt that she hadn't heard from either her parents or Chelsea and Slade, despite the fact that she had written to them both sending her complimentary tickets and asking them to the first night.

They had all come to watch her in both her previous roles. Perhaps seeing her in two disasters was enough loyalty to expect from any family, she thought dismally, trying not to let the prospect of the ordeal in front of her intimidate her too much. And all at once it *was* an ordeal. Faint beads of perspiration broke out on her skin as she contemplated the enormity of the task ahead. How could she have ever thought she was good enough to play Hero? No wonder Rachel had been making such snide remarks to her! She would never get through the play without making some serious blunder; she knew it.

She was just beginning to panic in earnest, when the door opened and Simon popped his head round, smiling at her.

'Okay?'

Meg, who had finished her make-up, grinned back.

'Everything's just fine. And we're having a double celebration afterwards, I hear?'

'Yes. Helen is over the moon now that she's got her daughter. She sends you her love, Kirsty, and says you're not to worry—you can do it!'

Kirsty was appalled to find weakly emotional tears blurring her vision for a few seconds, but she was unbearably touched by Helen's kindness—to think of *her*, in the midst of everything that had happened to her, spoke of a depth of kindness rarely experienced.

'Oh, by the way, you know . . .'

'Time we were on stage,' Meg announced firmly, taking Kirsty by the arm. She was feeling dreadfully nervous, a whole flock of butterflies clamouring for release in her stomach, and she barely registered Simon's unfinished sentence as Meg ushered her out of the room and back stage.

Rachel was already there, her normal expression hidden beneath her Beatrice.

'Right,' Simon instructed softly behind them, and in the concerted move towards the stage, protected by the closed curtains, Kirsty barely had time to wonder where Drew was.

During the initial part of the first scene Kirsty had little more to do than speak briefly and then remain in the background, which gave her ample opportunity to study the other actors as they entered part-way through the scene. They all looked unfamiliar in their costumes—Kirsty still hadn't got used to the difference they could make. She stiffened as she studied Claudio, her eyes widening as they lifted to his face. Only it wasn't Rafe's face, it was Drew's. Her heart

started to thump erratically. What was Drew
doing playing Claudio?

She found out during the first interval. Rafe's
sore throat had proved more serious than had
been expected and he had been told by his doctor
that if he went on stage he risked losing his voice
altogether.

'Wasn't it lucky that Simon was able to come
back to direct?' Cherry chattered enthusiastically
as she helped Kirsty to change ready for the
wedding scene, 'otherwise Drew wouldn't have
been free to play Claudio. There you are,' she
announced, fastening the dress. 'Very nice—
almost like a dress rehearsal for the real thing,'
she added a grin, 'although Drew's hardly likely
to do a Claudio on you!'

'No,' Kirsty agreed hollowly. It was true he
wasn't, for the very simple reason that he had no
intention of marrying her in the first place.

Knowing that she was playing opposite Drew
increased her nervous tension, and Kirsty was
actually trembling when she went back on stage.
A vague sense of unreality seemed to possess her,
so that she wasn't entirely sure what was real and
what was merely play-acting. Drew's cool,
cynical eyes were real enough, and so was the
expression in them. Just for a moment Kirsty
actually felt she was Hero, unable to comprehend
why her husband-to-be was looking at her so
coldly. And then came his rejection of her.

Listening to the cold hauteur of those words,
Kirsty had no need to act. Her shame and pain
were real; her agony of mind at being so
misjudged evident in her expression as she spoke

her own lines in a voice that trembled with fierce conviction. The audience was forgotten; the other actors were forgotten; she was simply a woman in love trying to convince her lover that he was wrong. Gradually her trembling anxiety changed to scorching sarcasm; it was evident in her movements, and the curl of her mouth, underlined as she spoke her lines, fading away to nothing as she listened to Claudio's final denunciation before swooning away at his feet.

Somehow she managed to stumble off stage when the curtains closed. Cherry was waiting for her.

'Oh, Kirsty, you were marvellous! I actually cried!' she told her. 'I couldn't believe I could be so affected—you were a thousand times better than I've ever seen you before. You've stolen the show from Rachel,' she added with relish. 'She's furious! I've just heard her arguing with Drew. She says you deliberately upstaged her.' Cherry gave a gurgle of laughter. 'Drew wasn't impressed. Actually he didn't seem to be in a very good mood. Perhaps he's finding being on stage a strain.'

Kirsty was inclined to dismiss Cherry's comment as fanciful until her final scene with him. He did look strained, she acknowledged. Beneath the stage make-up his face was drawn in bitter lines. Was it because Beverley wasn't here and he still had to tell her that they were back together?

Kirsty forced herself to concentrate not on her own private pain but on the play.

The final scene was a very emotive one. Drew's

voice was raw with a feeling that brought the
ache of tears to her throat, until the moment
when he had to accept her in place of Hero.

He stepped forward, touching her arm, and
Kirsty started to tremble. In the seconds before
he kissed her she experienced an aching sense of
loss to know that they were simply acting two
roles and that the sensual brush of his lips against
hers was no more than a part of that acting. But
even that knowledge was not sufficient to prevent
her lips from parting beneath his, her body
swaying against him, her eyes closing as she
drowned in the fierce pressure of a kiss that made
her eyes sting with tears. And then it was over.
The rest of the play passed in a fog of unreality.
She took her bows with the rest of the cast, still
wrapped in the strangely numbing blanket which
had engulfed her the moment Drew released her.

As she made her way to her dressing room, the
applause of the audience still ringing in her ears,
all she wanted to do was to go back to her room
and sit re-living the precious memory of Drew's
kiss. She started to cleanse off her make-up
automatically, when the door opened and in the
mirror she saw Drew's reflection. He was still
wearing his costume, but like her had removed
his stage make-up.

'It's all right, Meg,' Kirsty heard him saying
calmly as the older woman got up to leave,
obviously thinking tactfully to give them some
time alone. 'I just came to tell Kirsty that I'll pick
her up outside in fifteen minutes.'

'Wasn't she wonderful?' Meg enthused. 'I
don't think anyone watching the pair of you

could have doubted that you were very much in love,' she added forthrightly. 'It showed. I can't remember ever seeing such a charismatic performance before. Poor Rafe,' she said with a chuckle, 'he's got a lot to live up to!'

Kirsty had intended to tell Drew that she wasn't going to the party, but she could scarcely do so with Meg listening. Instead she showered quickly and changed into the dress she had brought with her, her fingers stilling for a moment as she slipped it over her head. It was the cream dress she had worn the night she had first seen Drew. She hadn't worn it since, but it was the only thing she had that was suitable, and after all, only she knew what memories it aroused.

As he had promised, Drew was waiting for her outside, the Porsche gleaming luxuriously under the street lamps. Kirsty was glad she had worn her dress when she saw that Drew was wearing formal evening clothes.

'Simon normally makes a point of inviting several influential people to these do's,' he told her by way of explanation. 'It helps generate goodwill towards the theatre. He normally holds them at home, but because of Helen's pregnancy, this time he's hired a suite at the York Royale. Have you seen him since the play finished?' he asked her with curious abruptness.

Kirsty's heart started to thump uncomfortably. Why did Simon want to see her? Hadn't her performance been good enough after all, or worse still, had Drew suggested to him that in view of the fact that he was being reunited with Beverley it would be an embarrassment to them both if Kirsty remained with the company?

She managed to shake her head in negation, although it was impossible for her to speak.

'So I'm going to be the first one to congratulate you on a first-rate performance, am I?' Drew asked her in a metallically flat voice that seemed to hold neither approval nor praise.

'I was . . .' Just behaving naturally, were the words trembling on the tip of her tongue, but she managed to silence them, and Drew filled the gap by supplying sardonically,

'Just doing your job? Oh, you don't need to tell me that. I take back everything I said about your acting ability,' he added with a savagery that took her off guard. 'You've all the makings of another Rachel. For a moment there on stage you almost had me convinced. A word of warning, though. Actors are a hot-headed race. Carry on as convincingly as you were tonight and you'll have difficulty dislodging them from your life after the play is over.'

Kirsty didn't reply. She could not. A huge lump had formed in her chest. Her body felt heavy and tired; her head ached, and she had an overwhelming desire to put her head on Drew's shoulder and burst into tears.

'Nearly there. Looking forward to the coming adulation, are you?'

What would he do if she told him the truth? That she no longer cared about her career; that much as she enjoyed acting she lacked the driving intensity that would take her to the top and that right now all she wanted from life was to be Drew's wife and to bear his children. Of course the theatre would always draw her, she would never lose that, but she acknowledged that now she would never feel as intense about it as she had done.

Obviously not expecting a response to his question, Drew turned into the gates of the hotel and brought the Porsche to a halt outside the main door. A uniformed commissionnaire stepped forward to open the door for her, taking the tip Drew proffered as he drove the car away to park it. An attractive receptionist pointed out the way to the suite where the party was being held. It was completely self-contained, she explained, adding with an enthusiasm which at any other time Kirsty would have found thrilling,

'My sister saw the performance tonight. She just rang to tell me that it was absolutely super and that I must get tickets. I've never been a great one for Shakespeare, but according to her this was really something!'

Kirsty blinked a little as she preceded Drew into the crowded room. There were far more people in it than she had anticipated; Drew had obviously made an understatement when he mentioned that Simon invited a few outsiders.

Cherry came rushing up to them and hugged her enthusiastically, and soon other members of the cast were thronging round them, congratulating them and telling Kirsty that she had been superb.

'I don't know about bringing tears to the eyes of the audience,' Meg sniffed at one point. 'I was pretty close to them myself when you rejected her, Drew. It was all so emotional!'

'Perhaps it wasn't simply acting,' Rachel remarked maliciously, watching Kirsty's face.

'Kirsty darling, you were so good!'

Kirsty dragged her eyes from Rachel's face to stare in bemused disbelief at her aunt and her husband.

'Chelsea—Slade—but . . .' Her eyes widened even further when she saw her parents behind them.

Ann Stannard hugged her emotionally. 'Darling, I couldn't believe that was my little girl up there! I was so proud of you.'

'Me too,' her father agreed gruffly.

'But you never said you were coming. You didn't even acknowledge the tickets I sent you.'

'You'll have to blame Drew for that,' Chelsea told her, taking her sister's place to hug Kirsty warmly. 'He rang us and told us he wanted to surprise you. Although it seems that you have a surprise for us,' she added meaningfully.

'Yes, you naughty girl,' Ann Stannard chided. 'But Drew has explained to us that you didn't want anyone to know about your engagement until after the play opened, and that it was only because Beverley Travers guessed that you made it official.'

Drew had told her family they were engaged! Kirsty turned her head and encountered his grimly unsmiling face.

'Now that we've all said our hellos, why don't we give them a few minutes on their own?' Slade suggested. He was looking at Drew and an unspoken message seemed to pass between them.

'We can all get together later on at the hotel for a celebration worthy of the event.'

A little to Kirsty's surprise no one made any demur at Slade's suggestion. Even her mother seemed less inclined to fuss than usual, and Kirsty could tell that she approved of Drew, but then what mother wouldn't?

'Come on, Kirsty,' Drew's fingers touched her arm, 'have you forgotten that we still have things to talk about?' he asked in a low voice.

She hadn't, but why on earth had he complicated matters by telling her family that they were engaged?

She didn't realise until he pushed her gently towards the door that he intended them to have their talk away from the hotel, but by that time they were already out of the foyer and on their way to the dark shadow of the parked Porsche.

The road to Drew's farmhouse was familiar enough to her now for her to recognise it instantly, and as they traversed the short distance in silence, Kirsty had time to build up the anger that was all she had to sustain her through the coming ordeal. How dared Drew invite her family up here and then make a fool of her by announcing their engagement—an engagement which he knew would soon be over?

He assisted her from the car with his usual courtesy, but Kirsty could tell that he was unusually tense and distant with her. Perhaps he too was dreading the coming interview; dreading her making some sort of emotional scene. Well, he needn't be. She intended to behave with all the control at her disposal.

Even so, it was nerve-racking having him head her to the comfortable sitting room, with its cosy lamps. She refused the drink he offered her, watching miserably as he poured himself one. His hand shook slightly and the knowledge that he too was on the edge nearly destroyed her poise completely.

His glass was placed on the table before he had even taken a sip from it, his expression partially obscured as he turned towards the fire.

'Kirsty,' he began slowly, 'I want to . . .'

'No, Drew,' she interrupted firmly, praying she wouldn't let herself down now. 'I want to tell *you* something.' She had tugged her ring off as she spoke and proffered it to him on the palm of her hand.

'I do realise that now you've achieved your aim, there's no longer any need for me to go on wearing this, so I'd like you to take it back.'

'Achieved my aim? What the hell are you talking about?' The violence of his words robbed her of breath. 'Look, Kirsty,' he said impatiently, 'you're not on stage now. I brought you here so that I could make one last desperate appeal to you . . .' He ran unsteady fingers through his hair and Kirsty had an uninterrupted view of the tension and anguish in his face. Pain exploded inside her that he should feel like that for Beverley.

'You don't have to appeal to me to set you free, Drew,' she managed jerkily. 'I know you and Beverley were together in New York, I know . . .'

'You know nothing,' Drew broke in explosively, 'nothing at all.' His eyebrows snapped together suddenly. 'What do you mean you know we were in New York together? You know no such damned thing. She happened to be on the same plane as I was going out there, but apart from that I haven't seen her since she walked out of this house weeks ago—and anyway, what's Beverley Travers got to do with us?'

Kirsty gaped at him.

'But, Drew, surely the whole purpose of our engagement—of my being here—was to make Beverley jealous, so that you could get her back. You told me it was.'

'I did?' All of a sudden his expression seemed to have changed, losing some of its anguished tension and instead becoming curiously watchful. 'Then I'm afraid you're going to have to refresh my memory,' he told her quietly. 'When did I tell you?'

'The night you brought me here after you'd announced our engagement. I told you I knew you had an ulterior motive, and you agreed. Surely you remember? I told you there was simply no way I was going to help you.'

'I remember that bit all right,' Drew agreed in a very dry voice, 'but I . . . Tell me more about my motives in getting engaged to you, Kirsty,' he demanded thoughtfully. 'You guessed I had an ulterior motive, go on from there.'

'If it had been anyone else I would have thought they were just trying to protect me because you knew . . . I . . .'

'Because you were still a virgin and I knew it, whatever Beverley might care to imply, and I didn't want the rest of the cast believing you were my mistress, but of course I wouldn't be gentleman enough to do that—is that what you're saying?'

Put like that it sounded almost insulting.

'You were so angry with me in Winton,' Kirsty palliated. 'And with every right.' She bit her lip. 'I had no right to try and do what I did. It was unforgivable—and childish. I was wrongly cast in the Howard play, and . . .'

'Did it never occur to you that I might have another reason for forcing our engagement on you?'

Kirsty stared up at him, puzzled.

'Like what?'

Wry self-mockery gleamed in his eyes, his smile slightly mocking. 'My dear Kirsty, you are one very dense young woman. Come over here.'

Puzzled, she did as he bid, gasping as, when she got within arm's reach of him, he took hold of her shoulders, his hands sliding up into her hair as he drew her closer; close enough for her body to respond dismayingly to his proximity. Her lips parted automatically as his hovered over them, and then he was kissing her, gently at first, and more fiercely as his fingers tightened into her hair, tilting her head back, and her emotions ran out of control.

It was several breathless seconds before he released her.

'Doesn't that tell you anything?' he asked huskily.

Her tongue touched dry lips nervously.

'It tells me you find me desirable,' she managed at last. 'Even though I am a virgin.'

There was bitterness in the final words and she found herself back in Drew's arms, her chin held firmly so that she was forced to meet his eyes.

'Perhaps I ought to try a different tack,' he murmured dulcetly. 'When I kiss you, what do you feel? Merely desire?'

Kirsty's face flamed. 'I . . .' She struggled to break free of his arms, unsure of her ability to lie when he was looking right into her eyes. 'I . . .'

'Will it help if I tell you that I love you and have done since you walked out of my bedroom and caused havoc in my life—something I once swore I'd never allow any woman to do——? It's quite true,' Drew promised softly, 'so true that unless you say something quickly I'll be forced to prove it with actions rather than words. Have you any idea what it's been like?' he groaned suddenly. 'Wanting you, loving you, and all the time terrified of losing you?'

'Every idea,' Kirsty replied quietly. This time when his eyes searched hers she felt no need to hide her feelings.

'When?' he asked softly, but she knew what he was asking.

'Probably from the first time you touched me. I told myself it was merely your experience coupled with too much to drink, but deep down inside I know it wasn't, and then you got at my part as Hero and I hated you as I'd never hated anyone before. You see, I thought you were trying to trap me into making a fool of myself so that you could dismiss me from *Much Ado* and your life, with one doubly humiliating blow.'

'When in reality I was trying to tie you to me

with as many strings as I could, praying that in time I could make you love me. I already knew you wanted me,' he murmured, enjoying her blush. 'But as you were ten years younger than me and still a virgin I couldn't simply use sexual magnetism to trap you into a marriage you might later regret. But every time I thought I was making headway I came up against a brick wall.'

'Because I thought you were using me to make Beverley jealous!'

'Didn't it occur to you ever that if I was I was using pretty drastic action?' he asked. 'And you still haven't told me you love me,' he reminded her.

'Don't you know?'

'How should I? Because you responded to me physically?' he mocked gently. 'It was like wine to a man yearning for water. God, I wanted you, but I was terrified of losing my head; getting drunk on the wine of physical desire and frightening you away for ever. I want your love as well as your desire, Kirsty, and permanently—I'd never settle for anything less.'

'You won't have to.'

The shy words fell into a pool of silence which lasted so long that Kirsty thought after all she had misunderstood him and he didn't love her, until she looked up into his face and saw the raw hunger mingled with a relief that found an aching response inside her.

'Dear God,' he exclaimed piously, 'I feel as though, having attempted to climb it for years, I've suddenly reached the peak of Everest, and I can see the whole world spread out below it.'

'Was it worthwhile?' Kirsty asked mischievously.

'I feel so good I can hardly believe it's true. Perhaps you might convince me?'

Shyly at first and then with growing confidence, Kirsty slid her arms round him, lifting her face for his kiss. It was fiercely intense, burning away all the doubts and misunderstandings, and it left her breathless and weak with desire.

'I want to make at least one thing clear.' Drew was releasing her reluctantly. 'There was never anything between Beverley and me of a romantic nature. She wanted to back one of my plays—that was the reason we were meeting in Winton. She wanted to keep it a secret, but I had second thoughts—I wasn't so desperate for a backer that I needed to sell myself in exchange,' he told her frankly. 'Oh, and by the way—that crit which started the whole thing off?'

'Yes?'

'I'm afraid I have a confession to make.'

Kirsty waited.

'I didn't actually write it. Oh, I saw the play and made a few notes—you were no worse than the others and obviously very inexperienced; the person who wrote the crit from my notes got the names mixed up. The person intended to bear the full brunt of my criticism was the lead actress. I hear they dropped her from the play when it reached New York, but by the time I realised about the mistake it was too late to rectify it. That's why I asked Simon to give you a chance—although I must admit my reasons weren't entirely altruistic. I knew you'd make an excellent

Hero, but I also wanted to keep you where I could see you. When Beverley announced that we'd been sleeping together, I made the most of it. I only wish she'd been right,' he added throatily. 'These last weeks have been hellish frustrating, especially when every time I closed my eyes all I could see was you.'

'They haven't exactly been blissful for me either,' Kirsty told him shakily. 'I loved you so much . . .'

'Show me.'

It was half an hour later before Drew reluctantly released her. Her small moan of protest was smothered by his mouth, before he pushed her away gently.

'Having waited this long, I think I can wait until you become Mrs Chalmers. Don't look like that—it won't be very long, I promise you, and now we'd better get back to that damned party before your father comes after me with his shotgun!'

It was early in the morning before the party finally broke up. Kirsty would far rather have spent the time alone with Drew, but she acknowledged the wisdom of returning to join the others. He had been surprised and then delighted when she told him that once they were married she would probably give up the stage, apart from the odd temporary role, perhaps, filling in when vacancies came along.

'Not entirely, I hope,' he had counselled her. 'I want a partner, Kirsty, and I want you to be happy.'

'I'll never have the dedication to get to the top,' Kirsty told him honestly, 'and I no longer want to.'

'Kirsty, I've got a bone to pick with you,' Chelsea interrupted, wandering over to join them, her arm linked with her husband's. 'You told me you weren't going to fall in love until you were at least twenty-six,' she reminded her niece, 'and now I won't have enough time.'

'What for?'

'Why to produce a little flower girl, of course,' she grinned. 'Still, there is John Charles . . .'

'Not unless he accompanies her down the aisle in his pram,' Drew put in firmly. 'I'm not waiting long—and certainly not long enough for him to learn to walk. I couldn't,' he added huskily, with a look for Kirsty that melted her bones to fluid.

'Something tells me we're de trop,' Slade murmured sotto voce, 'and besides . . .'

'Besides what?' his wife enquired as he led her discreetly away.

'I've just realised how long it is since I've been alone with you, Mrs Ashford,' he murmured wickedly. 'Drew and Kirsty don't have the monopoly on romance, you know.'

'I don't think they'd agree with you, somehow.' They both looked across the room to where Kirsty's head rested on Drew's shoulder.

'No second thoughts?' Drew asked.

'Just one.'

Kirsty felt him stiffen and relented immediately, delighting in the power she had over him.

'Mmm. I'm wondering if I made the right

decision allowing you to bring me here. Oh, Drew,' she told him, her eyes suddenly darkening, 'just think—if we'd stayed at the farmhouse, by now . . .'

'We'd have been lovers,' Drew finished for her. 'A special licence and soon we can be. I want it as much as you, Kirsty—more, perhaps,' he added wryly, 'but I want you as my wife; tied to me so firmly that you can't change your mind.'

'I won't,' she promised against his lips, joy flooding her heart and mind. He loved her. Really loved her!

He started to laugh.

'What's the matter?' Kirsty demanded half fearfully.

'Nothing. I'm just thinking that Shakespeare, were he to have witnessed our behaviour these last few weeks, would probably have called it *Much Ado About Nothing*—don't you agree?'

She was still laughing when he silenced the sound with his mouth.

 **ROMANCE**

How to join in a whole new world of romance

It's very easy to subscribe to the Mills & Boon Reader Service. As a regular reader, you can enjoy a whole range of special benefits. Bargain offers. Big cash savings. Your own free Reader Service newsletter, packed with knitting patterns, recipes, competitions, and exclusive book offers.

We send you the very latest titles each month, postage and packing free – no hidden extra charges. There's absolutely no commitment – you receive books for only as long as you want.

We'll send you details. Simply send the coupon – or drop us a line for details about the Mills & Boon Reader Service Subscription Scheme.
Post to: Mills & Boon Reader Service, P.O. Box 236, Thornton Road, Croydon, Surrey CR9 3RU, England.
*Please note: READERS IN SOUTH AFRICA please write to: Mills & Boon Reader Service of Southern Africa, Private Bag X3010, Randburg 2125, S. Africa.

Mills & Boon
the rose of romance